Menpachi Fracture, Double Reef

Field Guide to

Caves and Karst of Guam

By Danko Taboroši

BESS PRESS

3565 Harding Avenue
Honolulu, Hawai'i 96816
toll free: (800) 910-2377
phone: (808) 734-7159
fax: (808) 732-3627
e-mail: info@besspress.com
www.besspress.com

Acknowledgments

I would like to thank Dr. John Jenson for giving me the opportunity to study and enjoy the karst of Guam. Thanks for your friendship, guidance, and help, and for the long talks in the field. Among those to whom I am also grateful are Dr. H. G. Siegrist, Jr., for introducing me to island geology, and for the constant support masked by witty sarcasm; Mr. Silas Mountsier and the Dragomir Nikolitch Charitable Trust, for their trust and assistance; the US Geological Survey, for funding the research project from which this book spontaneously emerged; the Guam Legislature, for its support of local research through the Guam Hydrologic Survey program; David Vann, for being a driving force over the years as both a friend and a colleague — thank you for all the ideas, support, hikes in the karrenfelds, and lunches. My appreciation to Curt Wexel for sharing his wealth of knowledge, and to Mauryn Quenga, John Jocson, and Karel Smit for the adventures at WERI, help and fieldwork. Many thanks go to Dolores Santos, Norma Blas, and everyone at WERI for their help; and to Dr. John Mylroie, Dr. Jim Carew, Dr. Ivan Gill, and the teams from Mississippi, South Carolina, and Puerto Rico for their insight and collaboration. Thanks to Brent Tibbatts, Lisa Kirkendale, Nicole Scheman, Heather Tinsman, Carissa Canepa, Allison Palmer, and Jenn Coleson-Dolph for their friendship, thoughts, and company in the field. My appreciation to Todd Pitlik (DAWR) for the flights, to Braxton Plunkett for underwater photography, and to Matt Howes for showing me the submarine caves. I am thankful to Mike Ward for his spirit and for bringing fun into the caves. My sincere gratitude to Brett and Kathryn Wallace and Tosca for the exciting times we had caving and rappelling; and to Aubri and Lynda Jenson, Cole Herndon, and Grace Garces for company in the field and help with surveying. Thanks so much to Dishu Parmar for leading me to Ritidian Cave, to Dr. Mark Lander for showing me the caves in Asiga, to Greg Castro for taking me to Castro's Cave, and to Dave Lotz for crucial help. I am also indebted to the US Navy, US Air Force, US Fish and Wildlife Service, Perez Bros. Co., Hawaiian Rock Products, and private landowners for graciously allowing me to roam their property in pursuit of caves. To those who did not permit access, thank you for not shooting when I trespassed. Sincere thanks to Joan Swaddell for being my liaison on UOG campus and a true friend. I would like to thank Michele Tan and the Kondo family for being my hosts when the bulk of this book was written, and Žakalin Nežić for the meticulous manuscript review. Much appreciation goes to Vigor Majić and Petnica Science Center — za prvu pećinu i uvod u nauku. To my parents, Slavko and Branka, and my sister, Ivana — hvala vam što ste me pustili da odem ovako daleko, pazili i mazili preko sedam mora, za posete i puteve koji su me održali, za ljubav. Last, but not least, I wish to thank Justin Udovch and Amanda G. Sanchez for their friendship, support, and thoughts, and for every single day on Guam.

Table of Contents

This field guide to the caves and karst of Guam has its origin in the author's graduate thesis research in environmental science at the University of Guam. Readers—or rather, *users*—of the guide will readily recognize it as a labor of love. The wealth of detail contained in it reflects not only the author's devotion to his science, but his passion for adventure and his pleasure in sharing both. Mr. Taboroši's good fortune in finding a thesis project so congenial to his temperament and interests was exceeded only by my good fortune in finding a student with the enormous energy and dedication required to survey and document every significant cave and karst feature he could locate during the three-year span of his thesis project. The scope and accuracy of this guide attest to Mr. Taboroši's extraordinary stamina and dedication. His long and varied list of acknowledgments also shows that his talents also include a sociable disposition and propensity for the kind of teamwork essential for sustained productive fieldwork in the earth sciences.

Users of the guide will also see that Mr. Taboroši has struck a laudable balance between scientific content and accessibility to the non-specialist. His guide will therefore be of value to a wide array of users ranging from scientists and engineers to teachers and students at all levels in earth science and hydrology, to conservationists and recreational cave explorers and hikers. Professional users will find rigorous and exhaustive discussions of the scientific aspects in the related papers Mr. Taboroši is currently publishing in professional scientific journals. The diagrams and photos in this guide, however, give it a textbook quality that goes well beyond the scope of most field guides. Educators and recreational users will find it an informative source on the basic geology of Guam and, in particular, the characteristic features of the kind of karst terrain found on Guam and similar islands.

Finally, those who use this guide to its fullest by actually visiting the places or studying the features documented in it will learn for themselves why the author regards Guam and its environs with such affection. Like all the islands of the Pacific, it contains places of exquisite natural beauty, and has a unique and fascinating legacy of natural and human history. If each person who makes use of this guide derives only a fraction of the pleasure that Mr. Taboroši and I have gained from the work that produced it, they will be amply rewarded indeed!

John W. Jenson, Ph.D.
Associate Professor of Hydrogeology
Water & Environmental Research
Institute of the Western Pacific
University of Guam

INTRODUCTION

SCOPE OF THIS BOOK

This book is a field guide to the limestone areas of Guam, their spectacular karst topography, and numerous caves. Its purpose is to help you enjoy Guam's outdoors while learning about its geology.

1/2 SCIENCE, 1/2 ADVENTURE

The book begins with an introduction to the general geology and hydrology of Guam. Since karst features are all formed by water, the organization of this book follows the journey of water through a karst terrain. It begins at the land surface and proceeds underground and out to the ocean, with sections on the epikarst, surface flow (streams and rivers), sinkholes, caves, and coastal karst. Interspersed with the scientific information are guides to specific places on Guam: narrow gorges, deep sinkholes, spectacular caves, soaring cliffs, isolated beaches, hikes, SCUBA diving spots, and kayaking trips. By describing Guam's fun outdoor spots and activities in an appropriate scientific context, this book not only informs you about places to go and what to do, but also explains the complex geology behind Guam's stunning natural beauty.

FIELD GUIDE

This field guide is designed for people who are willing to explore on their own. It points you in the right direction, but does not lead you step-by-step to the goal. Rely on your own exploratory skills and topo maps in addition to written instructions, which are purposely concise and not detailed due to the sensitive nature of many sites involved.

☑ *CAVES, HIKES, DIVE SITES...*
Text in the colored boxes provides field information about specific places and outdoor activities on Guam. This includes directions to caves, trails, dive sites, etc. The text in each box ends with a note in brackets referring to a map on pp. 90-97 of this book where relevant locations are labeled and GPS coordinates are provided. Icons denote the following legend items:
- ☑ easy or average difficulty
- ☒ difficult, sometimes no trail
- ⊙ coasteering, average difficulty
- ⊗ coasteering, very difficult
- 🕐 go only at low tides/calm seas
- ① trip is one-way, drop off vehicle
- ☼ too dangerous if raining
- ★ demands experience
- ☊ rock climbing/rappelling

TOPOGRAPHIC MAPS AND GPS

Locations of all sites described in this book are shown on topo maps (pp. 90-97) as numbered red dots. Trailheads and other places with car access are shown as lettered blue dots. Small white dots denote trails, if any. GPS coordinates of most trailheads, waypoints, and destinations are also listed. Exact locations of certain caves are not published because of conservation and safety concerns, but appropriate contact information is provided. Maps at the end of this book are portions of USGS 1:24,000 scale maps and bear no latitude/longitude labels. Carrying full-size maps is essential for hikers, especially those planning to explore on their own.

SCIENTIFIC TERMINOLOGY

Scientific terms are used throughout this book, and are explained in the glossary on pp. 98-101. Learning some of them can help you better understand geologic processes shaping Guam. The metric system is used throughout, except for driving distances, which are given in miles. Unit abbreviations and conversions are listed on p. 101.

1

What Are Caves and Karst?

WHAT IS KARST?

The word "karst" refers to features and terrain where some of the rock has been dissolved by water. All features formed by dissolution, from the tiny raindrop marks on rock surfaces to the largest caves, are collectively known as karst features. They can form only in soluble rocks, the most common of which is limestone (composed of calcium carbonate, $CaCO_3$). Water is able to dissolve limestone primarily because of atmospheric carbon dioxide (CO_2), which, when added to water, makes it slightly acidic and gives it solvent power.

WHAT IS UNIQUE ABOUT KARST?

Because the rocks in which karst features form are soluble, they cannot support much surface water flow. In karst terrain, rainwater and streams tend to dissolve their way downward and disappear into holes in the rock. This is why karst areas usually lack surface streams. Instead of flowing at the surface, the water moves underground, via pores in the rock, small voids and conduits, and caves. The replacement of surface drainage by underground drainage is one of the defining characteristics of karst topography.

WHAT ARE CAVES?

Caves are holes in the ground. More specifically, they are natural underground voids, which people can enter. There are several types of caves, the most common of which are karst (solution) caves. Karst caves are formed by the water dissolution of limestone or similar rocks. As water moves through caves, it dissolves away the rock walls and enlarges the caves. Additional factors shaping karst caves are erosion and collapse. Most caves on Guam are karst caves, and this book refers to them simply as caves. The exceptions are artificial caves (WWII era tunnels) and some sea caves, which are created by wave erosion, not dissolution. Other types of caves around the world are lava caves (formed by lava cooling around lava flows); ice caves (formed in glacial ice); and talus caves, which occur at the bases of mountains and cliffs, and are simply confusing series of voids among piles of loose boulders.

WHAT IS CAVING?

Caving includes entering, visiting, and exploring caves. It is done for adventure, sports, science, or just fun. The scientific study of caves is called speleology.

WHAT IS LIMESTONE?

Limestone is a sedimentary rock consisting mainly of calcium carbonate ($CaCO_3$), which commonly occurs in two mineral forms: calcite and aragonite. It is a soluble rock and often has high porosity. The deposition of limestone occurs in marine and freshwater environments, by accumulation of $CaCO_3$ shells and skeletons of various organisms. When these deposits become exposed to freshwater and atmosphere (as is the case on islands and coasts), or become deeply buried (as in the interiors of continents), they undergo a series of changes and become limestone.

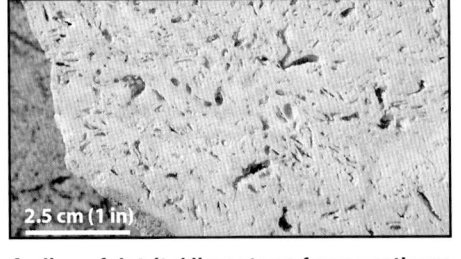

2.5 cm (1 in)

A slice of detrital limestone from northern Guam. Calcareous algae and other fossils have been dissolved by fresh water, leaving behind small voids.

Hiking in Karst Areas of Guam

HIKING

Hiking is an enjoyable way to explore Guam. There are many beautiful trails on the island, and many spectacular ones are in karst areas (northern Guam and parts of southern Guam). They are described throughout the book, especially on pages 82-89.

COASTEERING

Coasteering is a combination of coastal hiking, rock climbing, and swimming. Basically, it is navigating the coastline by scrambling over the coastal rocks, when possible, and by swimming, when it is not. Exciting and fun, but very demanding and potentially dangerous, coasteering requires dealing with challenges normally not encountered in simple hiking. These include negotiating tides and rough seas; traversing extremely jagged coastal rocks; climbing vertical cliffs; getting in/out of the water and over reefs while pounded by waves, and being alert for unpredictable surf and weather patterns. On Guam, the remoteness of the coastal regions from the nearest road is an additional challenge. Some coasteering routes on Guam are described on pages 82-89.

SAFETY

Always tell a designated friend exactly where you are going and when you expect to return. Park your car in a visible place, remove valuables, and leave it unlocked. If you get lost, stay calm, climb to higher areas, or locate the coastline. Avoid going alone and overexerting yourself. In coastal areas, you must know by which route you plan to return to the nearest road. Let experience and judgment be your guide.

WEATHER

Guam's climate can make hiking difficult. Because the days get very hot, it is best to leave early and avoid walking during the midday heat. In karst areas, there are no rivers or waterfalls where you can cool off. Rain makes limestone very slippery and hiking difficult. When caving, even a drizzle can be a huge problem (see next page). When coasteering, knowing tide schedules and weather conditions is crucial; therefore, such activities must be planned accordingly. Tide tables are available from dive shops. Be aware of changing weather conditions. Sunset time on Guam varies from 5:27PM (January), to 6:34PM (July).

FOOD AND LIQUIDS

Tropical heat can dehydrate you quickly, so bring along at least 2 liters of liquid per person. Sandwiches, sushi rolls, and fruit make excellent field lunches.

CLOTHING AND GEAR

Sturdy footwear is essential. Long pants, a short-sleeved shirt, a hat, and rain gear are recommended. Sturdy water shoes, swimsuits, gloves, strong and waterproof sunblock, a life vest, and a helmet should be worn when coasteering. A GPS unit and topographic maps are very useful, and so are a cell phone, snorkeling gear, and a flashlight. For caving gear, see page 5.

LAND ACCESS

Places mentioned in this book have no known access restrictions, unless otherwise specified. For information about access to Navy property, call 339.5208; for Air Force, 366.8005; for the Guam National Wildlife Refuge, 355.5096; and for other land, call the Dept. of Parks and Recreation at 475.6296. Always ask for permission when approaching private land. In privately owned coastal areas, stay on the shore.

IS CAVING DANGEROUS?

Although caving is potentially dangerous, with knowledge, proper precautions, and the right equipment, you can prevent most accidents, and your caving experience can be safe and exciting. Strength and physical agility are not necessary if you start with small and easy caves and progress according to your abilities. On your first trips, always go with experienced cavers!

SAFETY AND HAZARDS

There are numerous causes of accidents in caves, and you should be familiar with them. It is extremely important to let someone know where you intend to cave and what time you expect to return. Prior to entering a cave, leave your car keys outside and inform everyone in the group where they are hidden. That way anyone is able to go get help if an accident occurs. In caves on Guam, falls are the single greatest risk, and can result in anything from a minor bruise to instant death. Move slowly, think about your future moves before you make them, never jump, and don't be afraid to ask for guidance or assistance. Falling objects pose another danger. Loose rocks and boulders are common in caves. Try to stay away from anything that appears unstable. Avoid being directly beneath other cavers. If you dislodge or drop anything (no matter what it is) yell "Rock!" This is a universal signal to other cavers. You should also wear a hardhat as protection from small falling objects and bumping your head. Flooding is a serious risk in some caves, particularly those adjacent to volcanic areas. Never enter any cave if it has recently rained or looks like it might rain — especially those in Mt. Santa Rosa, Mataguac Hill, Nimitz Hill, and the Naval Magazine. Do not enter those caves during the wet season. When caving, look for evidence of flooding, such as mud stuck on cave walls or ceilings. Absence of mud on a passage floor may indicate violent flooding. If the water level in a cave rises, retreat, think, and don't panic. Getting lost is avoidable by slow, deliberate progression through a cave, familiarizing yourself with the cave, and staying near your fellow cavers. When you emerge from a small hole into a large area, study it and mark it by a glow stick or tape. When choosing a direction to proceed at intersections, study the location and mark it. Getting stuck in a tight passage is best avoided by sending a larger, more experienced caver through a "pinch" first. Be especially careful with vertical "pinches" where gravity works against you. Cave air (excessive CO_2) can be a risk. This is seldom a problem on Guam (Carino Sinkhole in Chalan Pago is one exception) but is not uncommon on the other Mariana Islands. If you notice that you are breathing harder than normally, immediately leave the cave. Hypothermia is a major risk in many caves, but not on Guam. Using a skin suit is a good idea in Guam's freshwater caves, where water temperature is 25-26 °C (77-79 °F). Finally, if accidents do happen, don't panic. Slow down and think. The psychological pressure caused by accidents can cause additional accidents. If you plan to become involved in extensive caving, take a basic Red Cross First Aid course. As a final note on safety, if all of this scares you — don't let it. With foresight, thought, and care, caving can be safe and lots of fun.

A muddy, stalactite-free ceiling is a clear indication of flooding (Almagosa Cave).

Caving on Guam - Equipment and Techniques

EQUIPMENT

Caving gear should be well made, tough, and waterproof. It will get wet, scratched, bashed, and dropped on an average caving trip. The best lighting setup includes a hardhat-mounted light (battery powered or carbide), and two tough waterproof flashlights. Spare batteries and/or spare carbide, and an extra bulb for each light are necessary. Light sticks, candles, and waterproof matches should also be brought. You must wear a hardhat for head protection. A bandana or a hat can make hardhat wear more comfortable. If your hair is long, bring something with which to tie it back. Clothing should be durable and not too loose. Kneepads, elbow pads, and gloves are needed in many caves, and a change of clothes is a good idea after leaving wet caves. Recommended footwear is hiking boots, but sneakers are OK, too. Other items to bring are a small pack for your gear, Ziploc bags, a garbage bag, water and food, marking tape, and a knife. Camera equipment should be carried in tough waterproof padded boxes. Always bring out everything you take into a cave.

TECHNIQUES

Deal with obstacles in a way you are comfortable with, and let experience be your guide. Be cautious and move slowly and deliberately. Think, and plan your moves before you make them. When climbing, try to move one limb at a time, leaving the other three in stable positions. A lot of climbing is done in relatively small spaces, while pushing in the opposite direction against the rock. This opposing pressure can keep you from slipping. It is generally easier to climb than descend, so be very careful when moving down. Don't jump inside caves. Be ready to assist your buddies. It is helpful to point your light

A narrow passage in Cool Cave.

at handholds and footholds when someone else is climbing, and avoid aiming your light into another caver's eyes. To get through many caves on Guam, it will be necessary to crawl. There are belly-crawls, hands-and-knees crawls, duck-walking, etc. In low places, be aware of rock formations overhead, and be very careful not to bang your hardhat against stalactites and destroy them. To avoid problems in "pinches," tuck in and secure your clothing and remove articles from your pockets; then go through in a way that won't demand impossible bending (some people are comfortable going head-first though "pinches"; some go feet-first). Step cautiously when walking through water, as there may be potholes and deep pools. These techniques refer to "horizontal caves" and are appropriate for exploring most caves on Guam. Horizontal caves are caves lacking pits and drop-offs. Caves with pits and drop-offs are known as "vertical caves" and require "vertical caving" skills — a different thing altogether. Some precautions regarding vertical caving follow.

VERTICAL CAVING

Although vertical caving takes more strength, endurance, and agility than horizontal caving, it is within the abilities of the average caver. However, you must be specially trained and equipped to do "vertical work," have your own equipment, and first practice on cliffs, trees, and similar places — not in caves. NEVER use the "hand over hand" method when moving up or down a rope in a pit. People are killed this way. Call Micronesian Cavers at 565.9128 for information on vertical caving and rappelling classes.

Rappelling in Devil's Punchbowl.

SNORKELING IN CAVES

Many caves on Guam are large, single-room caves with freshwater pools. Snorkeling in such caves can be very exciting. Pagat Cave (p. 52) is probably the safest cave for snorkeling, while others require a bit more caution, since they contain flooded passages and places where you could easily hit your head. Never free dive into a passage to see if there is air on the other side! If you do submerge, emerge very slowly. Hitting your head is a major danger, and light and reflection from the water surface can trick you into thinking that a ceiling less than an inch above the water is a safe place to come up for air. It is best not to submerge in any cave pools.

CAVE DIVING

This is the most dangerous form of caving; it requires a great deal of experience, expert knowledge, and special equipment. Cave diving without extensive training from an experienced cave diver is asking to get killed. To get a feel for cave diving, try some of the marine caves on Guam that do not require cave diving expertise (some are listed in this book). For more information, call one of the local dive shops that organize dive trips to some of these spots.

CAVE SURVEYING AND MAPPING

The exploration and study of caves requires understanding their layout. This is the main reason for cave mapping. A realistic map requires accurate measurements using surveying techniques. Surveys are performed by slowly moving through a cave from one point to another — measuring the distance, vertical angle, and the orientation between the two. The points are known as "stations" and must be within sight of each other. Essential mapping gear includes a compass, clinometer, and measuring tape.

UNDERSTANDING CAVE MAPS

The cave maps included in this book were made by cave surveying; they are not simple sketches. The symbols used on the maps are standard symbols used by the National Speleological Society. Listed below are some of the most common symbols:

cave wall	sand, soil
cliff, drop-off	gravel
stalactite	blocks, boulders
stalagmite	flowstone
column	water pool

Caving on Guam - Rules, Ethics and Conservation

SAFETY RULES OF CAVING

1. Tell a friend exactly where you are going and when you expect to return. Bring cave maps, if available, and check weather conditions.
2. Never enter a cave alone. The absolute minimum for a trip is 3 people; if one person is injured, one person can stay with him/her while the other goes for help. A group of 4 to 6 people is the optimum for a caving trip.
3. Always have 3 independent light sources with extra bulbs and batteries. All must be completely waterproof and durable.
4. Wear proper clothing. Leave your jewelry and sunglasses outside. If you wear glasses, secure them well. Gloves, kneepads, and elbow pads are recommended; hardhats are mandatory.
5. Never do anything you are afraid to do or consider unsafe. No one should ever be pressured to do anything.
6. Do not go caving if you are sick or "under the influence."
7. Begin with experienced cavers, learn your capabilities, and do not exceed your limits. Think, and go slowly.

LANDOWNER RELATIONS

Since cavers often must cross someone's land to reach a cave, prior permission must be obtained from the landowner. Be respectful of the land, do not litter, and after leaving the cave, inform the landowner.

CAVE CONSERVATION

Caves take thousands of years to form and damage done to them is irreparable. Care must be taken not to break or damage caves and speleothems (cave rock formations). When moving through a cave, follow the beaten path, do not walk on cave formations, and be cautious of delicate formations overhead. Do not touch the speleothems, and do not remove any from a cave, even if they are broken. Do not remove any rocks or artifacts from caves. Before entering a cave, take care of your bathroom needs. Do not smoke in caves, or harass, collect, or kill cave creatures. Everything brought into a cave must be taken out. If you see garbage in a cave, please take it with you. Some of Guam's well known and very beautiful caves have been made unappealing and ugly by trash.

Trash collected in Marbo Cave.

FOR FURTHER INFORMATION

Caving is a group activity. For further instruction and information on caving, get in touch with a local caving group, such as the Micronesian Cavers (565.9128). The GovGuam Department of Parks and Recreation (475.6296; www.admin.gov.gu/dpr/boonie/home.html), and Guam Boonie Stompers (653.2897) also organize caving trips. For scientific information about Guam's karst, check www.uog.edu/weri/karst. If you plan to get seriously into caving, consider becoming a member of the National Speleological Society (NSS). Their website is www.caves.org.

A view of volcanic terrain in Inarajan. Volcanic areas are characterized by grasslands, eroded badlands, prominent valleys, and volcanic rock outcrops, such as these black boulders — remnants of Miocene basaltic lava flows.

Guam is composed of two geologically distinct parts: southern Guam — a mountainous area of mostly volcanic terrain; and northern Guam — a limestone plateau.

HOW WAS GUAM FORMED?

Guam began as a series of submarine volcanic events. These volcanic episodes included underwater basaltic lava flows followed by pyroclastic explosions. Almost all of Guam's volcanic activity occurred underwater. As the island emerged, coral reefs began to form in shallow to intermediate depths. Subsequent tectonic activity resulted in a series of emergence and subsidence events (island movement up and down with respect to the relative sea level). This continues today, as well. During these tectonic events, carbonate marine deposits (coral reefs, reef debris, etc.) accumulated at different locations and at different rates. These ancient carbonates now make up different limestones that lie on top of the older volcanic basement.

WHAT ARE VOLCANIC ROCKS?

Volcanic rocks are formed when lava ejected from volcanoes cools. These eruptions are not necessarily violent and catastrophic, and many — particularly the underwater events — are slow and not explosive. Most rocks found in southern Guam are volcanic.

WHAT IS LIMESTONE?

Limestone is a sedimentary rock. This means it is deposited (formed) on the Earth's surface. It begins as marine or freshwater deposits of calcium carbonate ($CaCO_3$), created by living organisms such as corals, mollusks, some algae, and single-celled organisms. When they die, their shells accumulate on the sea floor. As the sea level changes, these deposits become exposed to fresh water and air. They undergo a series of changes and become limestone. Almost all rocks found in northern Guam are types of limestone.

GEOLOGIC HISTORY OF GUAM

The first submarine lava flows and pillow basalts were deposited during the Eocene and the Oligocene epochs — about 43 million years ago. Known as the Facpi Formation, they can be seen along the southwestern shore of Guam, from Inarajan to Merizo. Also in the Eocene and the Oligocene, explosive submarine volcanism created the volcanic rocks in Asan, Piti, Yona, and Santa Rita. They are known as the Alutom Formation. In the Miocene epoch, about 20 million years ago, underwater and subaerial volcanism deposited the rocks of the Umatac Formation, today exposed in Talofofo and Inarajan. The earliest deposition of limestone on Guam happened in the Oligocene and the Miocene, when most of the small limestone outcrops in southern Guam were formed. This includes Bonya Limestone (exposed in the Togcha River Valley and the Naval Magazine), Maemong Member limestone (in the hills overlooking Guam's southwest coast) and Talofofo Member limestone (isolated outcrops in Ipan and Talofofo). During the Miocene and the Pliocene, about 8-5 million years ago, extensive carbonate deposition occurred in the deep water of today's northern Guam, where Barrigada Limestone was deposited; and on the mountains of southern Guam, in Santa Rita and Agat, where reefs grew and eventually formed Alifan Limestone. By the Pliocene epoch, about 2.5 million years ago, northern Guam became shallow enough for reefs to grow, and subsequently became a giant lagoon bounded by a barrier reef. As the island was uplifted and the relative sea level dropped, this ancient barrier reef became the current cliffline of northern Guam, and the lagoon deposits became the interior of northern Guam, mostly covering the underlying deep water Barrigada Limestone. The cliffline and most of the limestone in northern Guam were deposited from that period until about 125,000 years ago, and are known as Mariana Limestone. The youngest limestone on Guam, less than 5,000 years old, is Merizo Limestone. It is found along the coast in Tarague and the south of Guam. Alluvial deposits, beaches, and modern reefs formed during the Holocene (recent) epoch. (See the map inside back cover.)

Mariana Limestone cliffs at Amantes Point were made from accumulated debris in an ancient lagoon. Former sea levels are recognizable from horizontal notches and cave development.

Geologic History of Guam

WHAT IS STRUCTURAL GEOLOGY?

Structural geology is the branch of geology concerned with examining the processes that shape the Earth's crust, its form, structure, and movement.

WHAT ARE FRACTURES & FAULTS?

Guam is in a tectonically active area; the rocks that make up the island are exposed to stress and strain. These forces cause the rock to crack and develop fractures. A fracture along which the separated bodies of rock have moved is known as a geologic fault. They exist on a variety of scales and some of the largest ones on Guam are longer than the island itself. The most prominent fault on Guam is the Pago-Adelup fault, which divides the island into the southern mountains and the northern limestone plateau. Fractures and faults can play a significant role in groundwater transport. For example, fractures can become pathways through which water moves very quickly, while faults can be obstacles blocking groundwater movement.

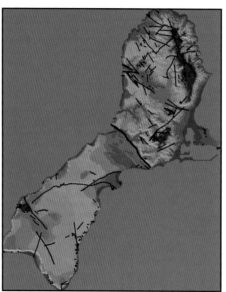

Map of Guam showing known geologic faults and fractures. Pago-Adelup fault is shown as the thickest black line. This mid-island fault divides Guam into two distinct geologic provinces: the northern plateau (limestone terrain) and the southern mountains (volcanic terrain).

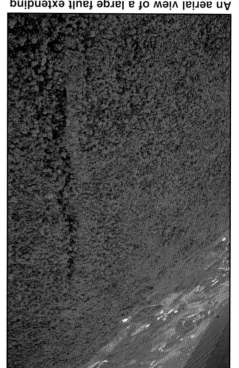

An aerial view of a large fault extending from Mt. Santa Rosa to the coast.

An aerial view of limestone cliff at Achae Point — an ancient barrier coral reef.

An aerial view of the area northeast of Fena Reservoir. This terrain exhibits cockpit karst — numerous sinkholes separated by limestone ridges and hills.

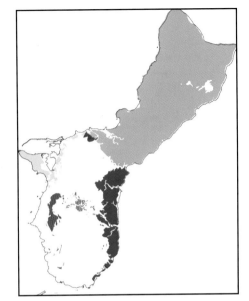
Limestone areas on Guam: the northern plateau is light blue; southeastern coast is dark blue; Orote and nearby outcrops are light green; central Guam's cockpit karst is dark green; Nimitz Hill is red; and southern mountain limestone ridge is brown. Volcanic areas are shown in white.

WHERE IS LIMESTONE ON GUAM?
Northern Guam is a limestone plateau. Sloping to the southwest, it is thinnest in its southern part (about 30m in Hagåtña) and thickest at the north end of the island (nearly 180m). Almost the entire surface of northern Guam, except for the volcanic hills of Mt. Santa Rosa and Mataguac Hill, is limestone. In southern Guam, limestone outcrops are scattered on the predominantly volcanic terrain. The entire southeast coast and the Orote Peninsula are made of limestone, as are the mountain ridge from Mt. Alifan to Mt. Lamlam and the lowlands northeast of the Fena Reservoir. Minor outcrops are found in the central part of southern Guam, the Nimitz Hill, and on the mountain slopes facing the coast in the southwest. All limestone areas on Guam were below sea level at some point in time, and all began as marine carbonate deposits. Because of tectonic movement and sea level changes, these areas became dry land.

Limestone Areas on Guam

Maemong Member limestone, composed of foraminifera and reef debris, is exposed on slopes overlooking Sella Bay.

Talofofo Member limestone, containing coral fossils, forms hills in central Talofofo.

Alifan Limestone on Mt. Lamlam.

Janum Limestone, near Catalina Point, is a deep-water foraminiferal limestone, mixed with volcanic debris from the nearby Mt. Santa Rosa.

The oldest limestone on Guam is known as the Maemong Member (Oligocene in age), and was deposited off-reef in relatively deep water. It is composed of foraminifera and reef debris, and can be seen on the slopes overlooking the coast of southwestern Guam. A unit known as the Talofofo Member (Miocene) probably grew as patch reefs in shallow water and today forms limestone hills in predominantly volcanic terrain in Talofofo. At approximately the same time, the Bonya Limestone (exposed in the Naval Magazine and the Togcha River) was probably deposited off-reef in moderately deep water; and the Alifan Limestone (capping the mountain ridge from Mt. Alifan to Mt. Lamlam) grew as a barrier reef. Both Bonya and Alifan limestone are highly variable and contain reef and lagoon deposits. An unusual type of limestone, named the Janum Formation, is exposed at a few spots in northwestern Guam. It is composed of foraminifera mixed with volcanic debris, and was deposited in deep water near volcanic highlands.

Barrigada Limestone in the walls of Perez Brothers Quarry, in Dededo.

Mariana Limestone argillaceous facies exposed on the coast of Inarajan.

Merizo Limestone, on the southern coast of Cocos Island.

Mariana Limestone at Amantes Point.

Most of northern Guam is composed of Barrigada (Miocene and Pliocene) and Mariana (Pliocene and Pleistocene) limestone. Barrigada, a white and friable foraminiferal limestone, was deposited in deep water and contains mostly benthic foraminifera. This formation, exposed at the surface in the center of northern Guam, is the principal aquifer unit and the main water source for Guam. Mariana Limestone grew on top of the Barrigada, as a barrier reef containing a large lagoon. Today, this ancient barrier reef is the cliffline, and the lagoon is the interior of northern Guam. Certain areas of Mariana Limestone (in the south of northern Guam and east coast of southern Guam) are unique, because they contain large amounts of volcanic debris derived from the adjacent volcanic terrain. These rocks are known as the argillaceous facies of Mariana Limestone. The youngest limestone on Guam is called Merizo Limestone. That found on the coast of southern Guam was formed from corals; that found in Tarague was formed from foraminifera.

Types of Limestone on Guam

Volcanic terrain in southern Guam. Volcanic rocks are not nearly as soluble as limestone; therefore, they can support the flow of streams.

John Jenson

WHAT IS HYDROLOGY?

Hydrology is the science dealing with the properties, distribution, and circulation of water in the atmosphere and on and below the Earth's surface.

WHAT IS THE HYDROLOGIC CYCLE?

Water vapor in the atmosphere precipitates and forms rain. Rain either forms surface streams, lakes, and other bodies of water; or it sinks underground to become groundwater. Some rainwater evaporates into the atmosphere, either directly or after being used by plants. This process is called evapotranspiration. Water that forms surface streams flows downhill and eventually reaches the ocean. Groundwater usually travels much slower, but it, too, eventually discharges from springs into surface streams and reaches the ocean; or discharges directly into the ocean from coastal springs. Water from the oceans (and land surfaces) evaporates and becomes atmospheric water vapor again. This vapor later precipitates as rain. This cycling of water in nature is called the hydrologic cycle.

HYDROLOGY OF SOUTHERN GUAM

When it rains in southern Guam, water joins one of about forty streams and rivers. It then flows on the land surface, downhill to the ocean. This is possible because the region is mostly volcanic terrain, and the rock is not very water-soluble or permeable. These rivers can have a very large flow during the wet seasons, yet can be reduced to trickles or even dry out completely by the end of the dry seasons. The area collecting the rain that feeds a particular river is known as its drainage basin. There are 19 drainage basins in southern Guam, the largest ones being the basins of the Talofofo, Ylig, Pago, and Inarajan rivers. The Talofofo River, Guam's largest, discharges an average of 1800 L per second. The smallest streams discharge about 50 L per second.

HYDROLOGY OF NORTHERN GUAM

The situation in northern Guam is very different. Northern Guam is a limestone plateau with virtually no streams or rivers. Rocks in northern Guam are water permeable and soluble, and the rain percolates into the ground instead of flowing on the surface. Driven by gravity, the water moves underground through air-filled fractures, voids, and conduits, and enlarges and connects them by dissolution. It reaches the groundwater level and a fresh groundwater body known as the freshwater lens. (See diagrams on the next page.) This "lens" of fresh water, recharged by rain, floats on top of the underlying seawater, which also easily moves through limestone. This relationship is based on buoyancy: fresh water ($1.000g/cm^3$), is lighter than seawater ($1.025g/cm^3$), and, therefore, floats on it. This freshwater "lens" is thickest in the center of northern Guam, and thins out toward the coastline. The body of rock "holding" the fresh water is known as the Northern Guam Lens Aquifer (NGLA) and is the primary source of drinking water on Guam. NGLA receives water from rain (recharge), and loses it from springs (discharge).

HOW DOES THE WATER "CREATE" KARST?

Karst forms in soluble rock, such as limestone ($CaCO_3$). Rainwater is unsaturated with respect to $CaCO_3$ and is, therefore, capable of dissolving limestone. As it falls on limestone surfaces and percolates down, it dissolves the solid rock and removes it in solution. This process creates karst topography and its various features (caves, etc.).

WHAT KINDS OF KARST FEATURES EXIST IN NORTHERN GUAM?

Karst features in Guam include the epikarst (heavily weathered rocks near the surface), sinkholes (points where water enters underground), caves (voids through which water moves underground), springs (points where water flows out from the aquifer), and other landforms. These features control the movement and storage of groundwater.

Limestone cliffs at Tarague and the northern Guam plateau. Limestone areas are characterized by forest vegetation, karst features, and the lack of valleys and surface waters.

Hydrology of Guam

WHAT IS THE NORTHERN GUAM LENS AQUIFER?

The Northern Guam Lens Aquifer (NGLA) is a limestone body in northern Guam that contains a fresh groundwater lens. It is the source of over 80% of Guam's drinking water supply. The lens is underlain by salty groundwater (basal part of the lens) and volcanic rock (parabasal part of the lens). The aquifer has several hydrologic zones (see diagram below). The unsaturated zone above the groundwater level is called the vadose zone. Rainwater percolates down to the lens through this zone to reach the groundwater table, below which is the saturated, or phreatic zone. It contains the freshwater lens, salty groundwater below it, and the mixing zone between them.

WHAT KIND OF AQUIFER IS THE NGLA?

Non-karst aquifers, such as sandstone, tend to contain water in voids between rock grains, and move it at steady rates and in predictable directions. The NGLA, however, is much more complex. It is a karst aquifer, and water within it moves through voids and pathways at highly variable speeds and directions, which are difficult to predict (see diagram below). For example, in a karst aquifer like the NGLA, water at one point in the rock can be barely moving through tiny pores, while just a few meters away it could be speeding like an underground river through a cave. Therefore, the movement, storage, accessibility, and quality of water in the NGLA are directly controlled by its karst features.

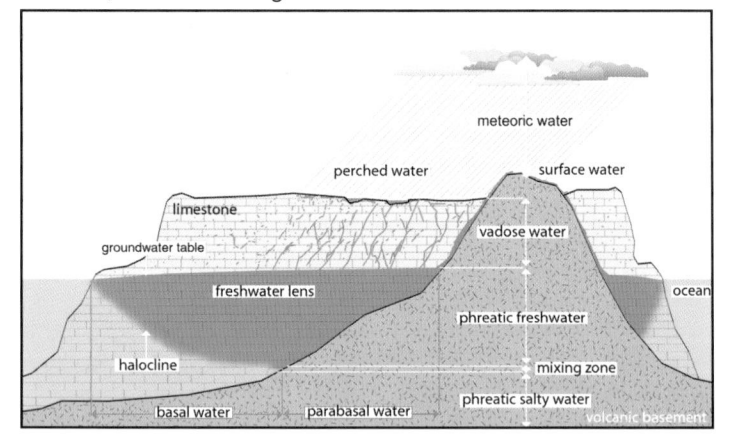

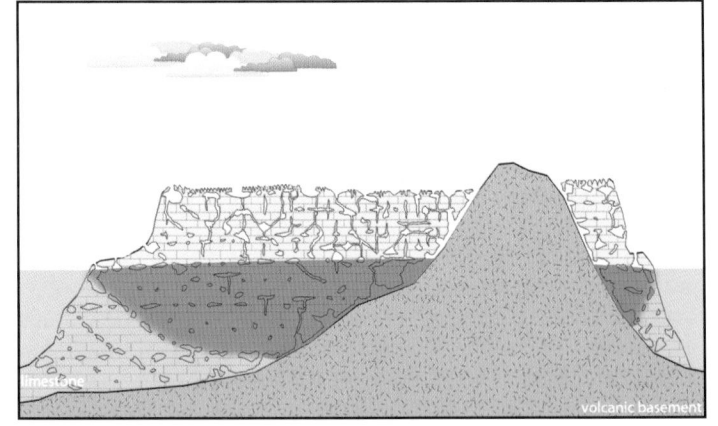

HOW DOES THE WATER MOVE IN NGLA?

The Northern Guam Lens Aquifer is recharged by rainwater. This water percolates into the rock and slowly moves downward through holes and cracks in the epikarst (vadose seepage) or flows into sinkholes and caves (vadose flow). Water flowing in caves and other conduits recharges the aquifer quickly; but water moving slowly through the rock can be stored in pores and voids in the vadose zone and can take months to recharge the aquifer. In the phreatic zone, water can also move quickly through karst conduits (conduit flow) and slowly via cracks and pores in rock (diffuse flow). Eventually, groundwater reaches the lens periphery and discharges from coastal springs.

HOW DO KARST FEATURES FORM IN THE NGLA?

Karst features are formed by unsaturated water, which is capable of dissolving limestone. After dissolving some limestone, the water becomes saturated and can no longer dissolve more rock. Therefore, most dissolution in the NGLA occurs 1) at the land surface, where rain first comes in contact with limestone; 2) in areas where the flow of water is focused; and 3) in areas where different waters mix and become unsaturated, due to complex chemical phenomena (this occurs at the top and the bottom of the freshwater lens). Voids are produced by dissolution, and further dissolution and collapse enlarges and connects them, ultimately forming a complex underground drainage system.

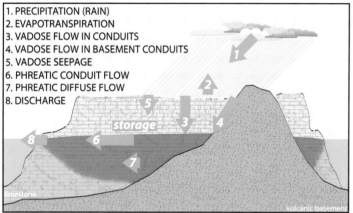

1. PRECIPITATION (RAIN)
2. EVAPOTRANSPIRATION
3. VADOSE FLOW IN CONDUITS
4. VADOSE FLOW IN BASEMENT CONDUITS
5. VADOSE SEEPAGE
6. PHREATIC CONDUIT FLOW
7. PHREATIC DIFFUSE FLOW
8. DISCHARGE

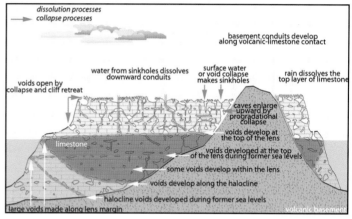

Soil pipes — soil-infilled pits in the epikarst, which allow rainwater to quickly percolate into the ground.

Epikarst is the top layer in a karst terrain; it includes karren (p. 20) and the heavily weathered bedrock just below the surface. As rainwater percolates through the epikarst, it dissolves the rock and makes distinct pathways in it. These pathways include soil pipes, enlarged fractures, shafts, etc. Water moves through them much faster than it moves through the rock itself. Thus, the pathways in the epikarst can speed up aquifer recharge. However, the numerous voids in the epikarst can also delay aquifer recharge, by storing water for weeks or even months.

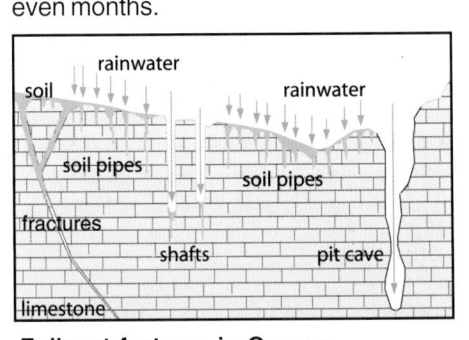

Epikarst features in Guam.

One of the most impressive vadose shafts on Guam is the spectacular pit cave at Amantes Point.

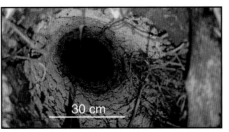

A nearly perfectly round vadose shaft.

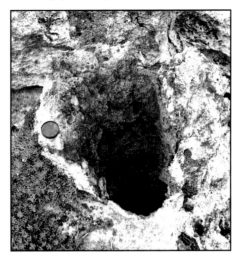

Vadose shafts, which are vertical cylindrical voids in the epikarst, represent the most efficient way for rainwater to reach the aquifer. They exist on a variety of scales, from small pits less than a meter deep to impressively large pit caves. They are also known as vadose bypasses, because they allow water to bypass the soil and the epikarst and flow directly to the aquifer. Vadose shafts are, therefore, extremely sensitive to pollution by solid and liquid pollutants. Nothing should ever be disposed of in a shaft.

☑ *AMANTES PIT CAVE*

Located within the Two Lovers Point tourist area, this 50m deep pit cave was created through dissolution by rainwater. The cave is easily viewed from a concrete bridge built over it. There is a bottom window in the cave, opening up to the cliff. The Department of Parks and Recreation prohibits rappelling here. [Map #1]

An old vadose shaft whose soil infilling lithified and turned into red-brown rock.

Shafts and Pit Caves

Karren

Surfaces of limestone rocks and outcrops come into direct contact with rainwater, which attacks them by dissolution. This process produces small dissolutional sculpturing, known as karren. These tiny, very diverse karst features are found on the surface of almost any limestone rock. Their shapes reveal much about the environment and the flow of water that created them. Some simple karren are tiny pits made by the constant impact of raindrops, while larger, more complex ones are shaped like pools, grooves, channels, etc., and are made by pooling and flow of water over rock surfaces.

Limestone forest inland from Double Reef, northwestern Guam. Rocks are heavily etched and covered by karren: solution pits, sharp points, and irregular holes. Landscapes dominated by karren are known as karrenfelds (fields of karren).

Long vertical channels found in the walls of Amantes Pit Cave are an excellent example of karren created by rainwater running down limestone walls.

Extremely jagged coastal pinnacles are not volcanic rock, as often assumed; they are limestone, heavily eroded by water and algae.

The growth of these "stalactites" in Ritidian Cliff Cave was influenced by algae and bacteria.

Biokarst "stalactites" leaning toward the cave entrance in a cave in Ritidian.

Limestone surfaces are not only shaped by water, but are also sculpted by organic processes involving bacteria, algae, fungi, and plants. The formations resulting from such processes are known as biokarst and are especially common and diverse in the wet tropics. The extremely jagged coastal pinnacles on Guam, for example, are a type of biokarst. The formation of these spectacularly irregular limestone features is thought to be a result of dissolution by rain and ocean spray, combined with the effects of blue-green algae, which live inside the rock and destroy it by boring into it. The algae give the rock its characteristic dark color. Some types of biokarst, however, form by deposition, instead of erosion. Some "stalactites" in the entrances of caves where daylight penetrates are often curved and even lean toward the light! These are not real crystalline stalactites as form inside caves, but are stalactite-like biokarst deposits created by algae and bacteria, whose uneven growth causes the curving.

Biokarst

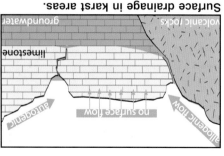

Surface drainage in karst areas.

Most karst areas on Guam lack surface drainage, because the limestone is too soluble and permeable to support surface water flow. However, surface water flow in karst commonly occurs when large volumes of water arrive in already formed streams from adjacent non-karst areas. This happens in southern Guam, and results in interesting karst features such as blind valleys, underground rivers, resurgences, gorges, etc. The streams arriving to a karst area from a non-karst area are known as allogenic; conversely, streams originating within a karst area are known as autogenic. Autogenic streams are rare in Guam.

Map of southern Guam and its extensive river network. The only rivers flowing on limestone are the Ylig, Togcha, Talofofo, Asalonso, Pauliluc, and Inarajan — which cross the coastal limestone belt in the southeast; and the Bonya, Maemong, Mahlac, and Tolae Yu'us, which briefly flow through limestone areas in central Guam.

Map of northern Guam, with its almost nonexistent surface drainage. The only exceptions are ephemeral streams on the flanks of Mt. Santa Rosa and Mataguac Hill, and the Fonte, Chaot, Pago, and Agana rivers in the area between Hagåtña and Mangilao, where the high clay content makes the limestone less permeable.

An aerial view of Agana Swamp, created in the former river valleys flooded by sea level rise. The Chaot River, flowing into, and the Agana River, flowing out of the swamp are remnants of the old river network.

An aerial view of the Chalan Pago area with its deep, but completely dry valleys. The valleys are remnants of rivers that have dissolved their way into the underlying limestone and were diverted underground.

Pulatar Dry Valley in Chalan Pago. Valley morphology is evident from the 100m contour line, but many sinkholes have diverted the former river underground.

Dry valleys are valleys with no permanent water courses. They are an evidence of former streams. On Guam, dry valleys are found in the southern part of northern Guam (Chalan Pago, Ordot, Hagåtña). The limestone in this area contains lots of clay derived from the nearby volcanic terrain. The high clay content made the limestone less permeable and capable of supporting a surface drainage network in the past. The rivers that formerly flowed in these valleys were diverted underground once sinkholes developed in valley floors. Sometimes, the valley walls can become completely eroded, leaving a string of sinkholes as the only evidence of a former river.

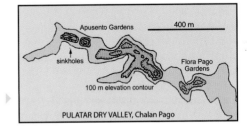

PULATAR DRY VALLEY, Chalan Pago

Dry Valleys

Blind valleys are valleys that abruptly end, usually facing a vertical limestone wall. Mt. Santa Rosa and Mataguac Hill, the only volcanic areas in northern Guam, have spectacular examples of blind valleys carved into their slopes. These deeply incised valleys look much like river valleys anywhere in southern Guam, except they never reach the ocean. Instead, they simply terminate at the bottom of the hill where the limestone terrain begins, and their water disappears underground. The water from the blind valleys continues to flow below the surface via stream caves.

An aerial view of Mt. Santa Rosa, a volcanic hill protruding through the northern Guam limestone plateau. Because volcanic rock is not permeable or soluble like limestone, rainwater flows in ephemeral streams down the mountain slopes in deeply incised valleys. Such valleys are known as blind valleys, because they end abruptly at the base of the mountain, where they reach limestone, and their streams "sink" underground into stream caves (p. 38).

Allogenic blind valley and its sinking stream.

Streams carried by blind valleys are known as sinking streams, because they disappear ("sink") into holes in the ground, known as swallow holes. After sinking, these streams continue to flow underground through cave passages. In northern Guam, the best examples of sinking streams are found on the volcanic flanks of Mt. Santa Rosa and Mataguac Hill. These streams are ephemeral (not permanent) and run only following a rainfall. Sometimes sinking streams do not disappear into distinct swallow holes, but gently sink into the valley floor. An excellent example of this is the Togcha River. It originates on volcanic terrain in the central part of southern Guam, but flows into a limestone area along the southeast coast. Once in contact with limestone, the water gently sinks into it and eventually disappears, leaving a dry riverbed. During wet seasons or following heavy rains, not all of the river water can sink into the limestone; some reaches the coast at the Togcha River mouth in Ipan.

The swallow hole at the end of the blind valley feeding Harmon Sink. Stormwater flows in a concrete culvert to this short valley, from where it quickly disappears underground.

Togcha River Valley. The photo of the water-filled riverbed (top) was taken 100m upstream from the place where the riverbed is completely dry (bottom).

Sinking Streams

25

Sinking streams can emerge after traveling some distance underground. Only two such rivers exist on Guam, and both are on the Naval Magazine, where limestone outcrops stand in the way of several allogenic streams. The Maemong River, flowing from the north, reaches a limestone ridge and disappears underneath it, into the Maemong River Cave. It resurfaces on the other side of the ridge, about 100m away, at the Maemong Rise. It then joins the Bonya River to form the Tolae Yu'us River, which disappears at the end of a classical blind valley into the Tolae Yu'us Cave. Its resurgence is 420m to the southwest.

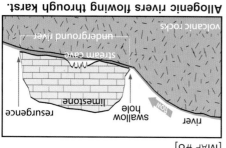

[Map #8]

Allogenic rivers flowing through karst.

Resurgence of Tolae Yu'us River, also known as Lost River. The river emerges from underneath a limestone ledge, after flowing at least 420m underground, via flooded cave passages. It then continues to flow on the surface, across impermeable volcanic terrain.

A collapsed limestone block and the vertical wall in the Togcha River Gorge. The Togcha is an allogenic stream, which means it begins on volcanic terrain, then flows onto limestone. On its way to the ocean, the Togcha crosses a limestone area along the southeastern coast of Guam, in which it has, over the millennia, cut a deep, narrow gorge.

Several rivers cross the coastal limestone belt in the southeast to reach the ocean. Most are large rivers with wide alluviated valleys. The Togcha flows at a steeper gradient and has incised a narrow gorge in Bonya Limestone, through which it flows on its way to the ocean. The gorge is a few hundred meters long, locally less than 5m wide, with vertical walls rising almost 50m.

☒① HIKING IN TOGCHA RIVER GORGE

The Togcha River Gorge offers spectacular terrain to hikers willing to make their way through water and dense vegetation. The two trailheads are at the Togcha River Bridge in Ipan (on Rt.4) and at Baza Gardens Sewage Treatment Plant (to reach it, go 1.9mi. on Rt.17 from Rt.4, turn left and continue straight 0.6mi. to the parking area, and walk down to the river). Start your hike at either end and drop off a vehicle at the other. Follow the river. [Map #7]

☑ KAYAKING UP TALOFOFO RIVER

For the true "jungle river" experience, explore one of the large southeastern rivers by kayak. Start at the river mouths/bays. Talofofo can be kayaked the furthest upstream. [Map #7]

Togcha River Gorge

Sinkholes are some of the most typical karst landforms. They are topographically closed depressions, internally draining, and vary widely in size and shape. There are two basic mechanisms by which they form: dissolution and collapse. Dissolution sinkholes occur when there is sufficient focused flow of water to drive the dissolution. The flow of water enlarges the sinkhole and its connections to the aquifer. This is a common situation on Guam in areas where limestone is found adjacent to volcanic rocks from which surface streams arrive. The second major type, collapse sinkholes, are created when roofs of some underground voids collapse. The origin of most sinkholes on Guam, however, is complex and involves numerous processes. Many closed depressions on the island are not true sinkholes at all but topographic lows that were originally deposited as such when the land surface was a coral reef. Sinkholes play a very important role in the recharge of the Northern Guam Lens Aquifer since they provide easy pathways for rainwater to reach the water table.

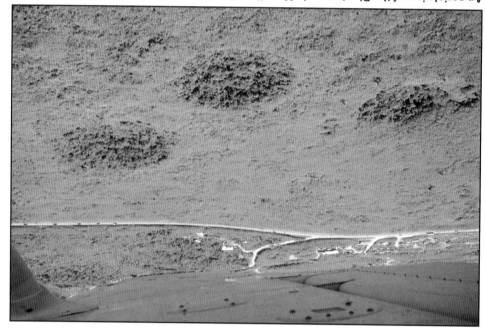

An aerial view of the Pinate area in Mangilao. The three sinkholes are over 100m across and 20m deep. Their origin is unclear, but it is entirely a subsurface phenomenon, since there is no evidence of associated valleys. They have formed either by large cave collapses (collapse sinkholes) or by slow subsidence (drawdown sinkholes).

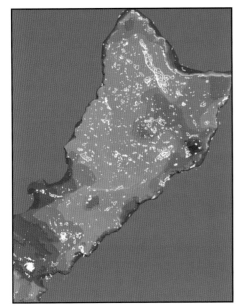

Map of sinkholes and other closed depressions in northern Guam. There are 1,252 identified depressions, ranging in depth from a few meters to over 30m and reaching lengths of hundreds of meters across.

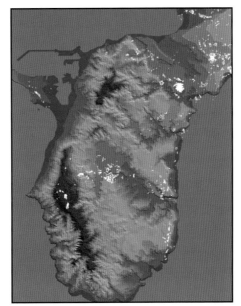

Map of sinkholes and other closed depressions in southern Guam. There are 197 identified depressions; the largest concentration of true sinkholes is in the central part of southern Guam, just northeast of Fena Reservoir.

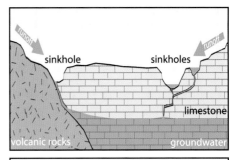

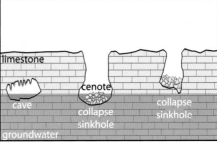

Two basic sinkhole types: dissolution sinkholes, made by surface streams (which, on Guam, arrive from volcanic areas) (top diagram), and collapse sinkholes, created by a cave roof collapse (bottom diagram).

SINKHOLES

29

Sinkholes can cause numerous environmental problems. When living on Guam, it is important to be familiar with some of the hazards, which include sinkhole flooding and collapse. While ponding of stormwater in sinkholes is a natural phenomenon, serious flooding can occur if a sinkhole becomes clogged by silt and debris or overwhelmed by the amount of runoff from paved areas. To minimize the risk of flooding, sinkholes should never be filled in or used as garbage dumps. Additional dangers are posed by sinkhole collapse: roofs of voids can suddenly collapse and destroy structures built on top of them. Prior to building in karst areas, existence of subsurface voids must be examined.

This sinkhole in Mangilao fills up with water after heavy rains. Such perched water indicates the sinkhole's diminished ability to conduct water to the aquifer, probably due to accumulated debris and overwhelming runoff from paved areas.

Ito & Minagawa Sinkhole, named after two Japanese stragglers who hid in it following WWII, is a 10m deep collapse sinkhole on a golf course in Ipan. It was formed by the collapse of a large cave, part of which remains.

A truck dumping a load of rocks and soil into a sinkhole as part of construction work on the south side of Mataguac Hill. This action is almost certain to cause flooding problems in the area, as the huge amount of rainwater collected by the volcanic slopes of Mataguac Hill will have lost its natural pathway to the aquifer.

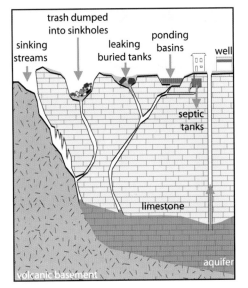

Sources of groundwater contamination.

Sadly, sinkholes are often used as garbage dumps. Carino Sinkhole in Chalan Pago is so polluted that the cave passages leading from it cannot be explored without special gear, due to excessive CO_2.

The Northern Guam Lens Aquifer is the primary source of drinking water for Guam. It is recharged by rainwater, which arrives from the surface slowly, by percolating through soil and rock; or quickly, by flowing through fractures and caves. Rainwater can collect pollutants at the land surface, or pick up buried contaminants (even if they are enclosed in containers, as these decay quickly when buried) and carry them to the aquifer. While the entire northern Guam is susceptible to aquifer pollution, sinkholes are particularly vulnerable, as they are often directly connected to the aquifer by preferential flow pathways. These are capable of delivering water to the aquifer quickly and without filtration. This problem is further exacerbated by people who dispose of waste and other contaminants into sinkholes — clearly the most sensitive places of all. This is a serious problem on Guam, where sinkholes are habitually used as garbage dumps. Nothing should ever be thrown into sinkholes, as doing so guarantees to pollute the aquifer.

Sinkhole Pollution

Tarague Well #4, a vertical-walled cenote.

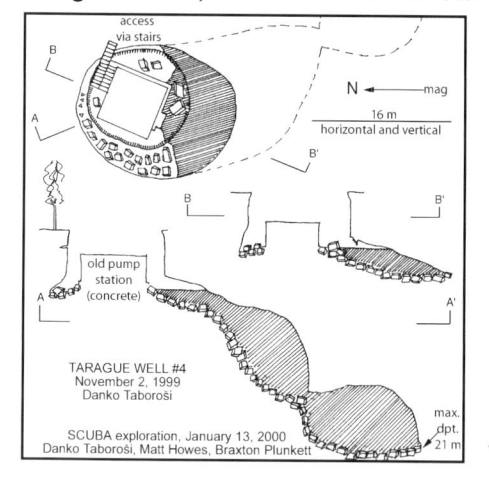

access via stairs

N — mag

16 m
horizontal and vertical

old pump station (concrete)

TARAGUE WELL #4
November 2, 1999
Danko Taboroši

max. dpt. 21 m

SCUBA exploration, January 13, 2000
Danko Taboroši, Matt Howes, Braxton Plunkett

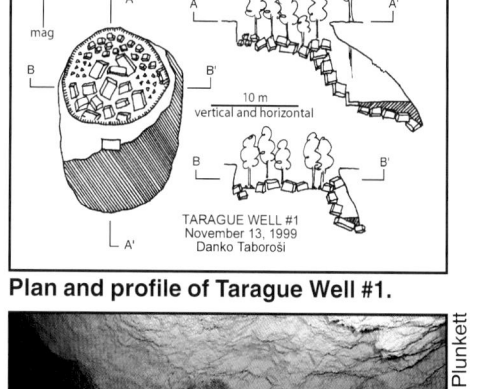

N
mag

10 m
vertical and horizontal

TARAGUE WELL #1
November 13, 1999
Danko Taboroši

Plan and profile of Tarague Well #1.

Braxton Plunkett

The submerged parts of Tarague Well #4 extend approximately 22m below sea level. The passages are highly unstable and dominated by collapsed rubble.

Plan and profile of Tarague Well #4.

Tarague Natural Wells (in Tarague on Andersen Air Force Base) are not wells, but a group of eight collapse sinkholes intersecting groundwater level. Such sinkholes are known as cenotes.

☑ ★ *FINDING TARAGUE WELLS*

Turn right just before reaching Tarague Beach on AAFB and drive to the concrete foundation on the right-hand side. Tarague Well #1 is in the jungle, about 35m southeast of that point. Well #2 is about 25m southeast of #1, just south of the grassy clearing. Well #3 is a bit farther down the road, on the left-hand side, roughly opposite Well #1 and is marked by a wooden sign "sinkhole." Tarague Well #4, which is fenced in and has a concrete stairway, is farther down the road, on the right-hand side. Well #7 is at the base of the cliff, southsoutheast of #4. Wells #6 and #8 are off limits; they are in the Small Arms Target Area, about 150m into the jungle, on the south side of the EOD road. Entering wells #6, #7 and #8 requires the use of ropes. Well #5, a very tight passage to the groundwater level, is too small for snorkeling. It is located just south of the row of telephone poles, in the brush near the beach (near the 7th pole). [Maps #3, #4]

Really Lost Pond in Mangilao.

Lost Pond, a sinkhole intersecting groundwater level, is one of Guam's most popular hiking destinations.

Lost Pond and Really Lost Pond, located in Hilaan and Mangilao respectively, are sinkholes with freshwater pools. The pools are not "filling" the sinkholes; they are water of the Northern Guam Lens Aquifer — exposed at the land surface because the sinkholes intersect the groundwater level. Only sinkholes deep enough to have their bases below the groundwater table can contain permanent freshwater pools.

☒ FINDING REALLY LOST POND

Really Lost Pond is in Mangilao, just south of the Hawaiian Rock Quarry. The best way to reach it is from Fadian Cove (see p. 86). Walk north along the shore to another small cove with a small beach. Then head northwest into the forest, where you will find two deep sinkholes. The first one is not deep enough to reach the freshwater lens; the second one is Really Lost Pond. It is located about 250m northwest of the beach, and the water in it is less than 1m deep. Both sinkholes contain interesting fractures and caves. [Map #6]

☑ HIKING TO LOST POND

To reach Lost Pond, park at Tanguisson Beach Park. Walk north along the coast to the interesting "mushroom rock" formations at Guma Fahou; proceed along a sandy beach to a rocky headland, another small beach, and the headland behind it. Next you will reach the beach south of Hilaan Point cliffs, where there is a sandy depression on the reef (Shark's Hole). From the beach, a short trail enters the forest and leads to Lost Pond, which is over 2m deep and great for swimming. There are 2 water caves to the north (see p. 61), and a few dry caves in the cliffs behind the pond. [Map #1]

Lost Pond and Really Lost Pond   33

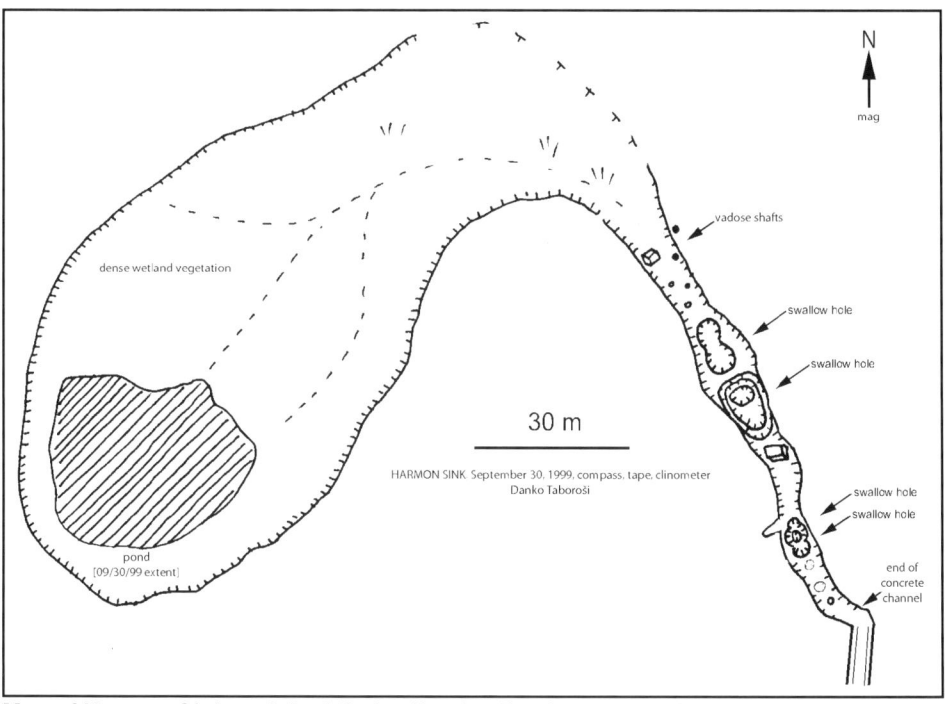

N
mag

dense wetland vegetation

vadose shafts

swallow hole

swallow hole

30 m

HARMON SINK. September 30, 1999. compass. tape. clinometer
Danko Taboroši

swallow hole
swallow hole

pond
[09/30/99 extent]

end of
concrete
channel

Map of Harmon Sink and the blind valley feeding it. Note the four successive swallow holes located along the valley. They receive stormwater coming from Guam International Airport via a concrete culvert.

Harmon Sinkhole is an elongated depression situated about 600m inland from Tumon Bay. It receives runoff from the Guam International Airport, via a concrete culvert and a classical blind valley. The valley feeds into the sink and contains four successive swallow holes. If one is flooded by a severe rain event, the next in line receives the runoff. The water from the Harmon sink discharges at the coast, in Agana and Tumon bays.

☑☼ **EXPLORING HARMON SINK**

Not exactly a prime hiking destination, Harmon Sink is an educational field trip for those interested in the hydrology of northern Guam. The easiest way to access the sink is from the Mai'Ana Hotel on Airport Road (Rt.10A). Walk to the culvert on the side of the road and follow it downstream, past the marshy area, staying left until you reach the blind valley feeding Harmon Sink. It is quite steep and has four swallow holes, 2m-4m deep. The valley ends in marshy vegetation with an ephemeral pond at the bottom of the sinkhole. [Map #1]

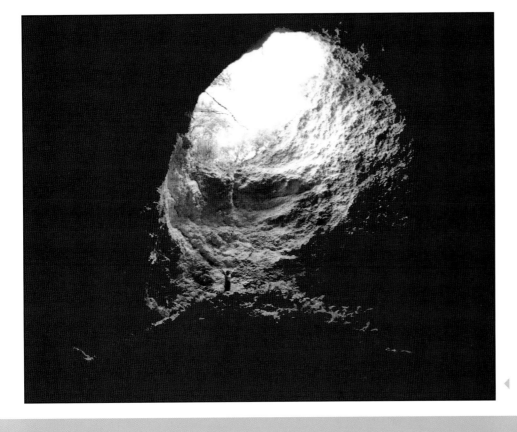

Devil's Punchbowl is a large fishbowl-shaped cavern inside the hill overlooking the Hilton Hotel in Tumon. With an entrance of nearly 20m across, it was opened by a roof collapse. The pit, 30m deep by 40m wide, has a small pool at the bottom and can be entered only by rappelling.

🎧 RAPPELLING IN THE PUNCHBOWL

For the best view of Devil's Punchbowl, park at the Hilton Hotel in Tumon. Climb up the hill behind the parking area and walk counterclockwise around the brush to a low fence and a small gate, behind which is the pit. To rappel, leave the Hilton, turn right onto San Vitores Rd., then turn right again into the old GMH housing area. Take the first right and continue to the last house, behind which is the pit. The house has suitable places to tie off. The drop to the top of the rock pile is 21m. Ascenders are needed to climb out. Because ascenders will get stuck on the overhang on the way out, a hanging ladder should be used to assist. [Map #1]

Devil's Punchbowl. The rubble pile in the center was formed by the roof collapse.

Devil's Punchbowl

A passage in Almagosa Cave. This stream cave drains part of the limestone highlands around Mt. Almagosa and feeds the Almagosa Spring on the Naval Magazine.

Caves can be defined as natural holes in the ground that people can get into. What most people think of as caves, however, are "karst caves" — holes in the ground formed via dissolution by water. This definition excludes WWII-era tunnels, hand dug caves, and cave-like holes in reefs — which are common on Guam but are not discussed in this book. Most caves on the island are true karst caves and there are hundreds of them. While all of them are, in some way, created by water, the actual processes involved can be very different, and each cave's history is unique. To really understand how caves are formed, it is necessary to distinguish between the two kinds of water underground: vadose and phreatic (see diagram on p. 16). Vadose water is the water moving down to the groundwater table. It is pulled by gravity through the vadose zone. Phreatic water is water below the water table, in the saturated zone. Caves on Guam can be divided into two groups based on the kind of water that created them: vadose caves or phreatic caves.

Caves of northern Guam. Locations of seventy-nine known caves are shown (red dots), but the true number is much greater. Caves are concentrated along the coast (mostly flank margin caves) and near the volcanic terrain at Mt. Santa Rosa and Mataguac Hill (stream caves).

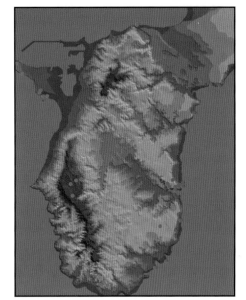

Caves of southern Guam. Sixty are shown on this map, but many more can be found, particularly in Matala and Asiga in Inarajan, Orote Peninsula, and Naval Magazine. Many southern caves are stream caves that were abandoned when their water supply was diverted.

Vadose caves (those created by vadose water) tend to be linear and complex, with long passages formed by the rapid flow of water, which enlarges and extends them. Three common types of vadose caves are pit caves (p. 19), fracture caves, and stream caves (p. 38). Phreatic caves (those made by phreatic water) on Guam tend to be globular and not complex. They typically consist of one or several rooms. They may be grand, but are not extensive or complicated, and lack long passages. This is because they form as unconnected voids by aggressive water slowly moving (diffusing) in the phreatic zone. The most common phreatic caves on Guam are known as flank margin caves (p. 39). It should not be assumed that all caves found in the vadose zone are vadose caves, or caves in the phreatic zone, phreatic caves. Relative sea level changed dramatically throughout geologic history. Because of these changes, a cave formed in the phreatic zone can today be high up in a cliff; and a vadose cave can be completely submerged by the ocean.

Entrance to Mataguac Spring Cave. It is a swallow hole of a stream fed by the runoff from Mataguac Hill and water from Mataguac Spring. Note the bamboo and debris transported by stormwater.

Stream caves are usually entered through swallow holes, but additional entrances, such as the one in Piggy Cave (above) can be created by a ceiling collapse.

The two most common types of stream caves on Guam: inflow caves, which are downstream continuations of surface streams (top); and outflow caves, which drain bodies of limestone (bottom).

Stream caves are formed in the vadose zone by the action of free-surface underground streams, which are often continuations of surface streams. They can be permanent, ephemeral, or abandoned. As aggressive water dissolves its way through limestone, its movement is often influenced by geologic structures, such as fractures and contacts with non-carbonate units. These can guide the development of caves. On Guam, stream caves usually develop along the contact between limestone and underlying impermeable volcanic rock, and tend to have long linear passages.

Flank margin caves form in the phreatic zone, along the perimeter of the freshwater lens (coastline) where fresh groundwater and salty groundwater mix. This mixture is aggressive and capable of dissolving large voids. The water does not move quickly through flank margin caves, as it does through stream caves. It does not flow; it slowly diffuses. This is reflected in the morphology of flank margin caves, which have large chambers but no long passages.

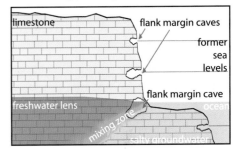

John E. Mylorie

Pagat Cave is a typical flank margin cave: it contains large chambers, but has no linear passages; it is vertically restricted; and its walls are covered by phreatic dissolution surfaces (walls and ceilings smoothened by dissolution under fully flooded conditions). Pagat Cave is discussed in detail on p. 52.

Flank margin caves are formed in the mixing zone along the island's perimeter. As the sea level changes, these caves can become exposed above the sea level or submerged below the sea level.

Stalactites often develop along ceiling fractures, where the water most easily percolates; stalagmites develop directly underneath (Ritidian Cave).

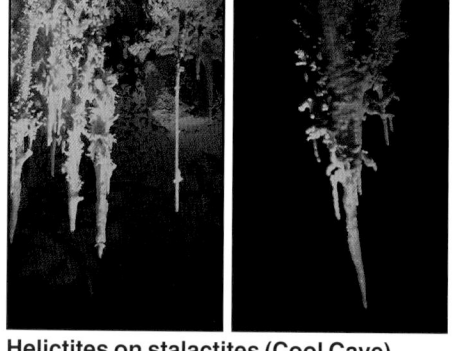

Helictites on stalactites (Cool Cave).

A straw with a helictite (Cool Cave).

Stalactites (hanging) and stalagmites (standing) are the best known speleothems (cave "decorations" formed by minerals deposited inside caves). Other speleothems include flowstone banks, rimstone pools, soda straws, cave pearls, columns, etc. They not only make caves aesthetically pleasing, but can also help you decipher the cave's history. Speleothems are most commonly formed by mineral calcite, precipitated from water saturated with calcium carbonate ($CaCO_3$) as it drips or flows in a cave. Speleothems take a very long time to form and should never be touched or taken from a cave.

Speleothems in Asiga North Water Cave.

The famous pictographs in Gadao's Cave in Inarajan are a Chamorro cultural treasure and one of the symbols of Guam.

WWII artifacts are not uncommon in caves on Guam. They should not be touched or moved.

The low entrance to a cave behind Ritidian Beach is thought to be an ancient Chamorro burial site.

The caves of Guam harbor numerous cultural treasures, from ancient Chamorro pictographs and pottery to WWII artifacts. The most famous pictograph caves are Gadao's Cave in Inarajan (p. 61), where the drawings are thought to depict a legendary encounter of chiefs Malaguana of Tumon and Gadao of Inarajan; and caves in the low cliffline inland from Ritidian Beach parking area (p. 59). Pieces of pottery are often found in caves with freshwater pools, indicating their use by the ancient Chamorros as water sources. In more recent history, caves provided refuge during WWII. The local Chamorro population sometimes hid in caves and even used some as churches (Gumayas Caves, p. 61). A US Navy radioman, George Tweed, hid in a cave from October 1942 to July 1944 (Tweed's Cave, p. 61). Following the war, Japanese stragglers hid in caves for many years. Bullets, grenades, and other war paraphernalia are often found in caves. They should not be touched, but should be marked by tape for safety.

Artifacts

Contact between basement volcanics and limestone in Awesome Cave.

Non-vertical stalactites indicate ceiling movement — probably a result of an earthquake (Asiga North Water Cave).

A highly unstable ceiling made of collapse boulders (Asiga South Water Cave).

When caving, make it a habit to notice and try to interpret various cave features; and examine the cave architecture and contemplate its origin. Long, tubular caves were probably formed by underground streams. Caves that have slanted and parallel ceilings and floors may have developed along fractures. Globular caves without long passages probably formed by dissolution by slowly moving water. Paying attention to cave features not only helps you to understand the geologic history of a cave, but it helps you to establish good safety practices. Various cave features can provide clues about a cave's stability and its likelihood of flooding. For example, a cave floor made of volcanic rock indicates that the cave was most likely formed by an ephemeral stream that flows along the volcanic-limestone contact. Such caves almost certainly flood during rain events. Occasional cave flooding is also indicated by smooth ceilings with few or no stalactites, and walls covered by mud. Passages formed in bedrock are more stable than those dominated by rubble.

Extremely jagged, "Swiss-cheese" dissolution features occur where fresh groundwater and sea groundwater mix (Fafai Cave). The mixing of waters usually makes the mixture very "aggressive."

Vertical fluting on a boulder in Awesome Cave indicates inflow of rainwater through the ceiling. This water is still "aggressive" and capable of dissolution.

Speleothems, which are formed in caves by precipitation, can be destroyed by dissolution. Typically, precipitation takes place in the cave atmosphere, and dissolution takes place underwater. With this knowledge and by recognizing the right features, we can sometimes reconstruct basic cave histories. For example, a stalactite found underwater can only mean that part of the cave was dry in the past, but later became flooded; a smooth ceiling without any stalactites may indicate that a room was entirely flooded in the past, and all of the speleothems were dissolved away (see photos on p. 39 and 53.)

Half of this large stalagmite in Ritidian Beach Cave (p. 59) has been removed by dissolution, leaving a neat cross-section behind. This indicates a complex cave history: one episode when the cave was above sea level, enabling stalagmite growth; another episode when the cave was below sea level, allowing dissolution; and the third (current) episode when it is again above sea level.

Interpreting Cave Features

Talofofo Caves are an extensive cave system located in the Mariana Reef limestone cliff overlooking Ipan. They are a popular hiking destination and some of the most visited and most accessible caves on Guam. There are seven caves in the complex, clustered around two collapse sinkholes. The sinkholes are two former caves whose roofs have collapsed, the natural arch surmounting one sinkhole being a remnant of a cave ceiling. The geologic history of these caves is somewhat puzzling, as they are on high ground and have no input of water besides rain; however, their size and shape indicate that they once received extensive stream input. It is possible that they used to be stream caves, which drained volcanic areas of central Guam through the limestone ridge into the ocean. As the terrain in central Guam was lowered by erosion, the runoff could have been diverted to the Talofofo River, leaving the caves as dry high ground.

Map of the Talofofo Caves complex.

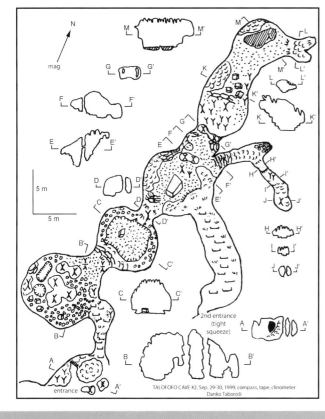

TALOFOFO CAVE #2, Sep. 29-30, 1999, compass, tape, clinometer
Danko Taboroši

Window Rock, a natural arch formed by the partial collapse of a cave ceiling, can be seen from Rt.4 in Ipan.

Talofofo Cave #2 is the most extensive in the complex.

Of the seven caves in the complex, caves #1, 3, 4, and 5 are very small tubular caves with soil floors and almost no speleothems. Cave #2 has four large, beautifully decorated chambers. Cave #6 is a 30-m long tube, extending through the limestone ridge and opening onto a cliff face overlooking the ocean. Cave #7 is a 32-m deep pit with two entrances and additional horizontal passages halfway down the pit.

☑ **EXPLORING TALOFOFO CAVES**
To find these caves, drive toward Talofofo on Rt.4A, 0.2mi. from the intersection with Rt.4. Park your vehicle on the right-hand side of the road and follow the trail uphill to the first fork. The trail bearing right leads to cave #7, a deep pit, which should not be visited without rappelling equipment. The trail bearing left from the fork leads to a collapse sinkhole, which has a natural arch overlooking the ocean and five caves around it. Cave #2 (the first you see when approaching) is the largest. A small trail heading north from #2 leads to the back entrance of #7 and to cave #6, a tunnel with a cliffside opening. [Map #7]

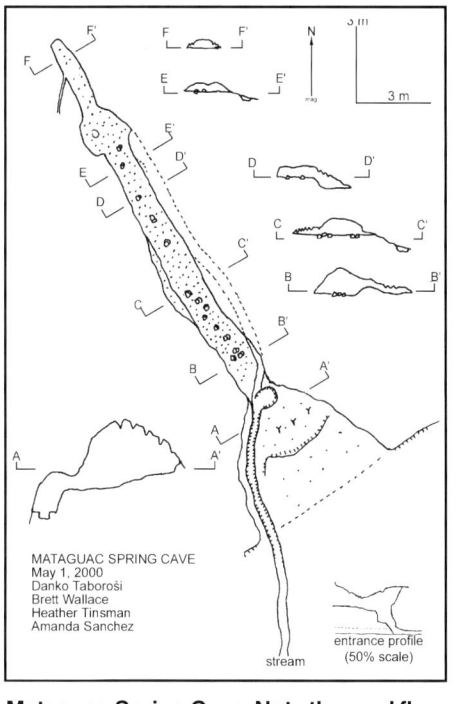

Mataguac Spring Cave. Note the mud floor and the narrow tributary near the end of the traversable passage.

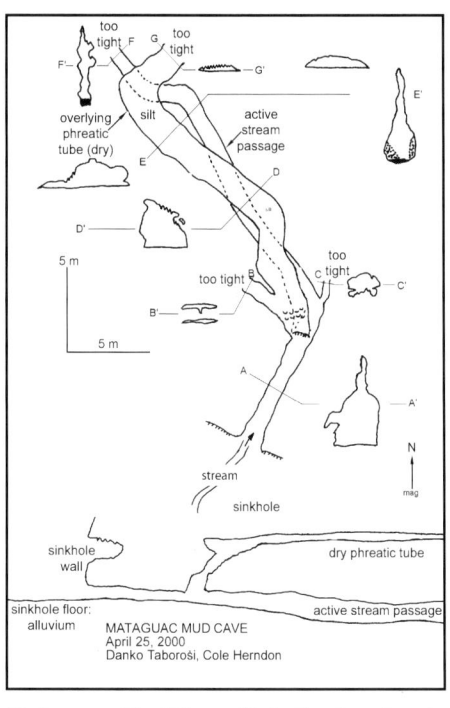

Mataguac Mud Cave. Note the two levels of passages: the top passage is a phreatic tube; the bottom one is a vadose canyon.

Mataguac Hill is a volcanic area surrounded by limestone. When it rains, surface streams form on the volcanic terrain and flow to the adjacent limestone where they sink into caves. Such caves are underground continuations of surface streams. On Mataguac Hill, caves tend to be very tight and muddy passages, without large rooms or many decorations.

☑☼ **MATAGUAC HILL CAVES**

Mataguac Spring Cave is easily accessible. Going north on Rt.1 in Yigo, turn left onto Milalaf Dr., 0.3mi. past Santa Lourdes Church, and then proceed to the Pacific Peace Memorial Park. Park there and walk northeast from the Peace Chapel to the bamboo grove and several WWII Japanese caves. Farther along the path are stairs leading down to a sinkhole and Mataguac Spring. From the spring, follow the water to the entrance of Mataguac Spring Cave. The other caves in the area, including Mataguac Mud Cave on southwest side of Mataguac Hill, are more difficult to reach. You can find them all by following and carefully examining the limestone-volcanic contact line around Mataguac Hill. [Map #5]

Almagosa Cave is a permanent (continually flowing) stream cave. It drains the Mt. Alifan limestone ridge and feeds the flashy Almagosa Spring, which is the entrance to the cave. The source of water flowing through the cave is both groundwater (collected by Alifan Limestone and evident from the cave's stream flow even during the dry season) and rainwater (evident by the spring's flashiness). Nearby Chepak Spring, 65m away, is part of the same cave system. There are rumors that Dobo Spring is also connected by traversable passages. The total explored length of the cave's main passage is 165m, the final 100m being located behind a siphon.

A large phreatic tube in Almagose Cave, feeding the Almagosa Spring. Water comes from groundwater in the Mt. Almagosa limestone area, via a complex system of progressively larger passages. The elliptical cross-section of this passage is typical of passages that periodically become fully flooded.

✿★ *ALMAGOSA CAVE*
This famous cave is marked on topo maps. It is located east of Mt. Almagosa, and can be reached by road. However, it is within the Naval Magazine, which is a highly restricted area where access is generally not granted. The Naval Magazine is very rich in caves. [Map #8]

Almagosa Cave

PROFILE

volcanic basement

(2 m)

pools and waterfalls (1 m)

volcanic basement

main entrance

scoured limestone floor

PLAN

N

mag

volcanic rock floor

2nd entrance

LUNCH ROOM

GREAT ROOM

10 m

10 m

pool

pool

continues

PIGGY CAVE
October, 1999
survey data by Curt Wexel
sketch by Danko Taboroši

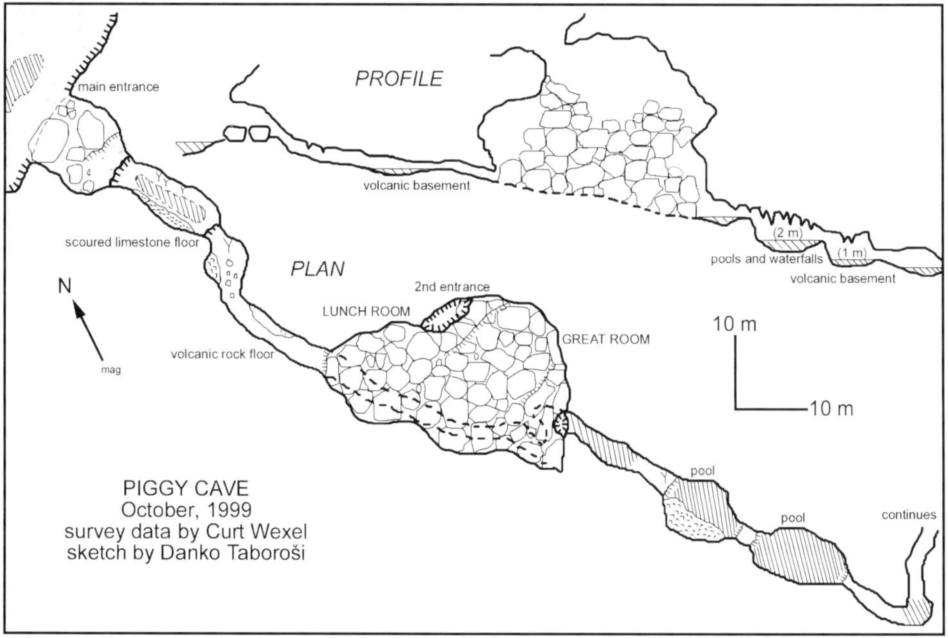

The profile and plan of Piggy Cave. Note the permanent large pools in the active stream passage: the pools remain full even during the dry season, because the floor of the passage is made of impermeable volcanic rock. The large rooms and additional entrances seem to have developed by the progradational collapse of the active stream passage.

Piggy Cave, in a sinkhole on the northeast side of Mt. Santa Rosa, is one of many ephemeral stream caves receiving runoff from the mountain's volcanic slopes. It is a long, tubular cave with a stream passage containing several rooms formed by progradational collapse. In addition to the main entrance — a swallow hole where the surface stream enters the cave — Piggy Cave has two more openings created by a roof collapse. A steep drop-off to the stream passage makes an etrier (or hanging ladder) necessary.

One of several permanent pools in Piggy Cave's ephemeral stream passage.

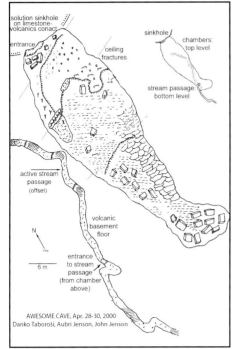

The plan of Awesome Cave. The entrance is located in a sinkhole on the contact between limestone and volcanic rock.

Active stream passage in Awesome Cave. Note the volcanic units (black) making up the floor.

Like Piggy Cave, Awesome Cave and its neighbor and a tributary, Interesting Cave, are ephemeral stream caves fed by runoff from Mt. Santa Rosa. Awesome Cave is special, because it contains a series of large dry rooms, undercut by the active stream passage. The rooms show evidence of having been flooded, possibly during former high sea levels. The cave's entrance is in a sinkhole southeast of Mt. Santa Rosa.

☼★ *MT. SANTA ROSA CAVES*

These caves are difficult to find, very dangerous for the inexperienced, and have access restrictions imposed by their owners. To visit these caves, join an organized caving trip with Micronesian Cavers (565.9128) or Guam Boonie Stompers (653.2897). These caves should be visited only in the dry season and NEVER if any rain is likely, as their passages can flood quickly and completely. [Map #4]

The profile of Awesome Cave. Note the series of large chambers undercut by a stream flowing on the volcanic rock base.

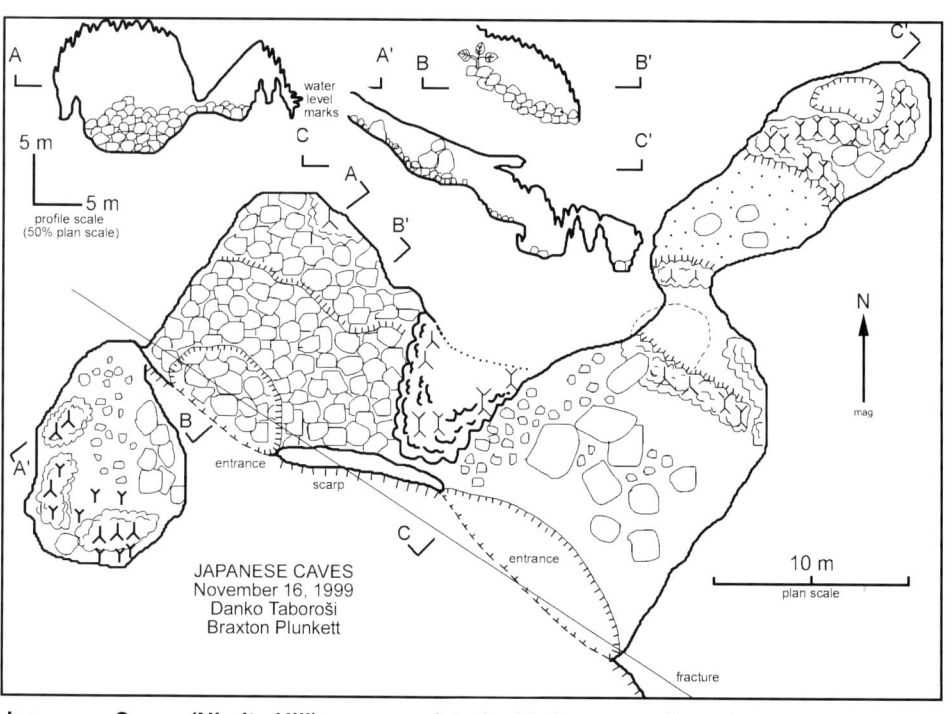

Japanese Caves (Nimitz Hill) are associated with fractures. Note the alignment of the cave's two entrances along a single fracture within a collapse sinkhole. Also note the steep, fracture-guided slope of the part of the cave along profile C-C'.

Nimitz Hill is a large block of Alifan Limestone, surrounded mostly by volcanic terrain and dissected by many faults and fractures. Being adjacent to volcanic units, from which focused surface water can arrive, and being full of fractures that can guide the movement of water, Nimitz Hill has a large number of complex caves. A simple walk through the forest on Nimitz Hill reveals numerous fissures, sinkholes, pits, and shelter caves. A more detailed look exposes larger caves, usually associated with fractures and sinkholes.

⊠ ☼ ★ *CAVES OF NIMITZ HILL*

Drive up Nimitz Hill on Rt.6 to DoD High School. Opposite the school, at the edge of the forest, is a directional sign to the Japanese Caves. Follow the short trail to the caves. Then make your own trail to look for the large number of other caves in the area. Carefully examine fractures and sinkholes to find new entrances. Micronesian Cavers (565.9128) is familiar with several caves in the area (Elvis' Pelvis, Admirable Cave, Birthday Cake Cave). [Map #8]

Cool Cave is a large, beautiful cave on the coastal plain in Asiga, Malojloj. It extends vertically for about 25m and contains several large rooms, connected by very narrow passages.

Beautiful speleothems in the main room of Cool Cave.

☑★ FINDING COOL CAVE

The trail starts on the north side of the Malojloj dump. Follow the trail to the cliff, where there is a fantastic view of the Asiga coastline. Then backtrack to a small trail, which branches off to the north and leads to a suitable place to descend the cliff. The trail becomes very steep, but requires no special equipment. At the bottom, where there is a large 15m tall limestone boulder, the trail continues south, to your right. Follow the limestone outcrop at the base of the cliff to an area where several large boulders lie scattered. The cave entrance faces west and is under one of them. Once inside, stay to the right and crawl through several extremely narrow passages to the larger rooms. (Many people will not be able to squeeze through.) It is absolutely necessary to use marking tape or glow sticks in this cave, as it may be difficult to find your way out without them. [Map #7]

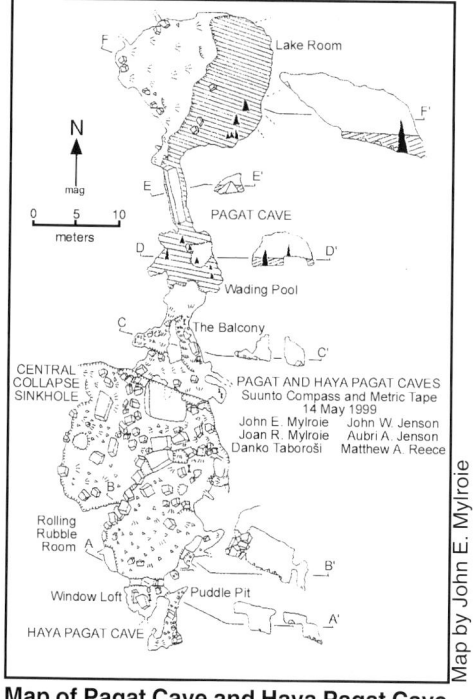

Map of Pagat Cave and Haya Pagat Cave and the collapse sinkhole between them.

Map by John E. Mylroie

Pagat Cave is a freshwater cave located in a limestone forest on a sloping coastal terrace in northeast Guam. It is accessed through a collapse sinkhole, which leads to two caves: Pagat to the north; Haya Pagat to the south. The caves were connected prior to the collapse of the central room, which is now a sinkhole. They are typical flank margin caves, dissolved out by the mixing of fresh and salty groundwater. Such caves have large globular rooms, but no long narrow passages, because their development was unrelated to rapid water flow. Water enters and leaves such caves by diffusion from and into the surrounding rock. Pagat Cave well illustrates that flank margin caves can develop without entrances and are not related to surface drainage. If the central sinkhole had not collapsed, Pagat Cave would have remained hidden. Flank margin caves become open to the surface only if their roofs or walls collapse or become eroded. There are probably hundreds of caves like Pagat on Guam, but they do not yet have entrances. Pagat Cave also illustrates the complex sea

level changes Guam has undergone. Its submerged stalagmites and flowstone could not have developed underwater, but must have formed during a sea level low; the smooth ceiling, devoid of any stalactites, was dissolved out during a sea level high. Cave walls and ceilings with smooth cusps and few or no speleothems, like those in Pagat Cave, are called phreatic dissolution surfaces and indicate a cave's formerly fully flooded conditions. The pool in Pagat Cave is fresh groundwater. As it floats on seawater in the ground, it responds to daily tides.

☑ HIKING TO PAGAT CAVE

The trail begins as a dirt road, on the east side of Rt.15, 6.7mi. north of its intersection with Rt.10. Park on the main road or anywhere along the dirt road and follow it. It gradually becomes a steep Jeep trail, then a hiking trail. When the trail forks, stay to the left. This very steep trail reaches a collapse sinkhole with two cave entrances: Haya Pagat Cave on the right; and Pagat Cave, which has a large freshwater pool, on the left. [Map #5]

A submerged room in Marbo Cave. Note the stalactites underwater. Since they can develop only in a cave atmosphere, they are a proof, in this case, of a rise in the sea level.

Marbo Cave, a flank margin cave on the northeast coast of Guam, contains a large freshwater pool. The cave is undergoing collapse. It appears to be connected to the ocean by non-traversable passages.

☑ **GETTING TO MARBO CAVE**
Driving from Mangilao north on Rt.15, turn right at its intersection with Rt.26. Drive downhill and take a left at the fork. Continue to the end, and park. Walk 50m down the steep trail to the cave. You can snorkel in this cave, but be very careful. Do not dive here! Another trail leads from the cave to the coast. [Map #5]

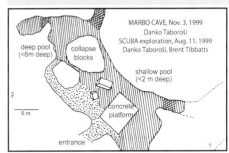

Plan of Marbo Cave.

Marbo Cave

Fadian Cave is a flank margin cave opened by a partial roof collapse. It is located at sea level and has a freshwater pool. This cave is extremely unstable.

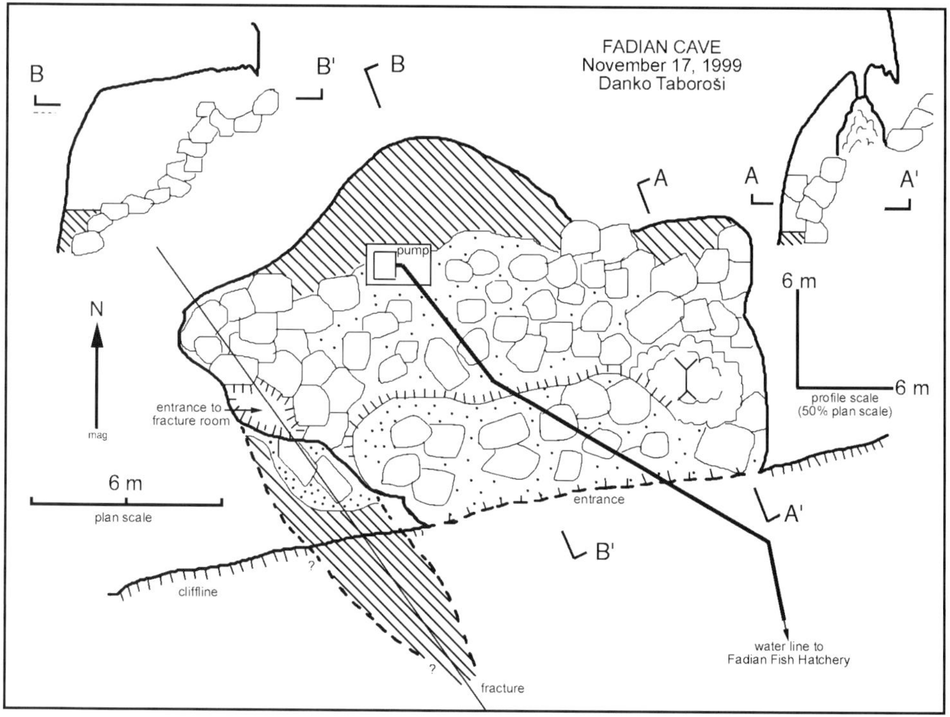

☑ **GETTING TO FADIAN CAVE**
Before visiting, you must obtain permission from the Guam Aquaculture Development and Training Center (734.3011). To reach the cave, heading north on Rt.15 from Mangilao, take a right onto Perez Park Rd., before Mangilao Methodist Church. Continue downhill to the GADTC fish hatchery. The cave is at the base of the cliff. [Map #6]

FADIAN CAVE
November 17, 1999
Danko Taboroši

N mag

6 m
plan scale

6 m

6 m
profile scale
(50% plan scale)

entrance to fracture room

pump

entrance

cliffline

fracture

water line to
Fadian Fish Hatchery

Fadian Cave, a collapsed chamber at the base of a limestone cliff. It intersects the groundwater table and is a freshwater source for the GADTC Hatchery at Fadian.

One of the passages that has developed along a fracture. Note the plant roots extending to the water level.

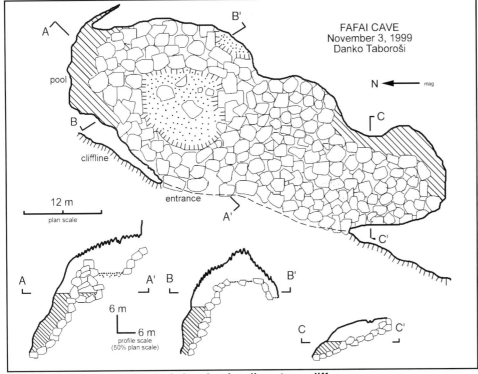

FAFAI CAVE
November 3, 1999
Danko Taboroši

A
pool
B
cliffline
entrance
A'
B'
N ← mag
C
C'

12 m
plan scale

6 m
6 m
profile scale
(50% plan scale)

A ⌐   ⌐ A'   B ⌐   ⌐ B'

C ⌐   ⌐ C'

Fafai Cave is a large collapsed chamber in a limestone cliff.

Fafai Cave is a large flank margin cave. It consists of a single large room, filled and almost divided into two parts by collapsed blocks and boulders. There are several freshwater pools with submerged passages.

☑ *HIKING TO FAFAI CAVE*

From Fafai Beach, located north of Gun Beach (p. 84), follow one of the short trails through the forest to the cliffline. Examine the cliffline until you find a large cave entrance, several meters up the cliff. Climb over the collapsed boulders to enter the cave. There are freshwater pools in the north and south ends of the cave. [Map #1]

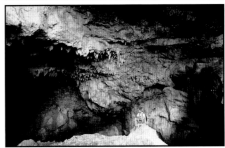

Large room in Fafai Cave.

Fafai Cave

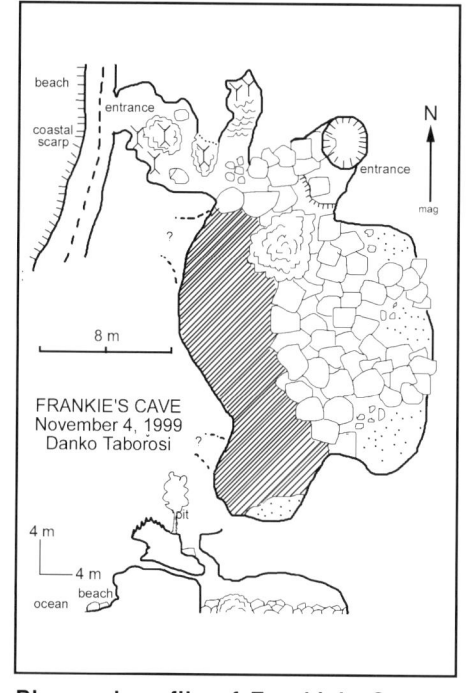

Plan and profile of Frankie's Cave, a coastal freshwater cave, dominated by collapse features.

The main entrance to Frankie's Cave is a small hole created by a partial collapse of the ceiling; the second entrance is in a coastal cliff.

Frankie's Cave is a small coastal cave just south of Double Reef Beach. Located at sea level, only 18m from the beach, the cave's single room contains a freshwater pool. The main entrance is a small hole in the ceiling, and most of the cave's floor is covered by collapsed rubble. A single narrow passage leads from the cave to a cliff opening overlooking the beach, 5m above sea level. This passage may have been a conduit discharging spring water at the coast until inactivated by a drop in sea level. There are additional passages in the submerged portions of the cave. This cave is located in a small cove where a freshwater spring discharges about 7.5 mil. L per day.

⊠ FINDING FRANKIE'S CAVE
Start at Double Reef Beach (see Double Reef hike on p. 85) and go south along the coast to the first small cove that has a large freshwater spring (Frankie's Cove). The low cliffline surrounding the cove contains one entrance to the cave, while the other entrance is in a small collapse pit, 10m inland. [Map #2]

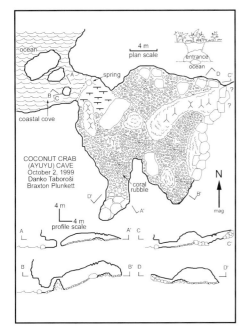

Plan and profile of Coconut Crab Cave, a freshwater spring cave and one of the largest coastal springs in Guam. Note the small cove, which may have been another cave room prior to its collapse.

Coconut Crab Cave. The channel leading from the cave was created by freshwater outflow, which stifled coral growth.

⌧ ⊕ *COCONUT CRAB CAVE*

At low tide and during calm surf, start at Double Reef Beach (p. 85) and follow the coastline south. The first cove is Frankie's Cove (p. 56). Continue south to the next small cove with a large cave entrance at sea level. A freshwater stream (best seen at low tide) emerges from the cave. The northeast part of the cave, filled by large boulders, is unexplored and could be extensive. Use a rope and marking tape to avoid getting lost in the maze of giant boulders. [Map #2]

Some of the coastal springs on Guam emerge from caves. The single largest coastal spring in northern Guam is at the Coconut Crab Cave, about 300m south of Double Reef Beach. The cave's entrance is at sea level, in a small cove with several large boulders. The cove may be a former cave room, which has collapsed. A steady stream of fresh water emerges from the cave at the waterline and is best seen at low tide. The cave's main room is about 30m x 20m x 4m high, and is divided by several flowstone partitions. The floor is covered by flowstone and coral rubble and the back wall consists of collapsed boulders, which can be crawled around in order to explore the inland extent of the cave. This cave discharges about 19 mil. L of freshwater per day. A related karst feature can be found by following the coastline north of Double Reef Beach. It is a beautiful natural arch surmounting a prolific coastal spring (see cover photo). The arch is probably a remnant of a cave similar to Coconut Crab Cave.

Coconut Crab Cave 57

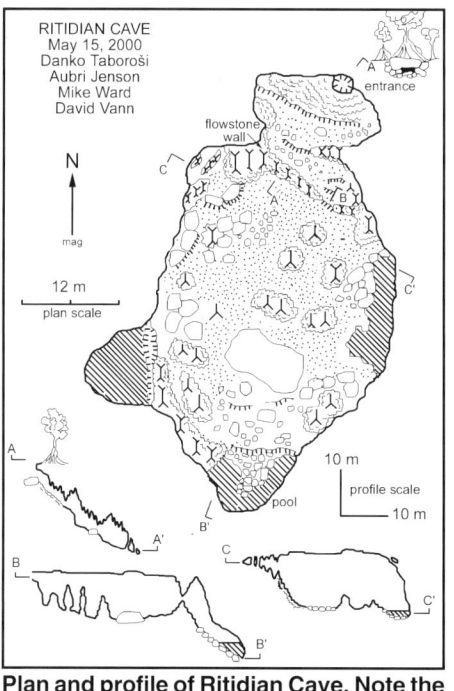

RITIDIAN CAVE
May 15, 2000
Danko Taboroši
Aubri Jenson
Mike Ward
David Vann

flowstone wall

N
mag

12 m
plan scale

10 m
profile scale
10 m

pool

Plan and profile of Ritidian Cave. Note the tiny entrance relative to cave size, and the massive flowstone deposits, which have almost closed off the main room.

Large stalagmites in the main room of Ritidian Cave. Note the lack of stalactites above, an indication of frequent ceiling collapse.

Freshwater pool in Ritidian Cave.

The largest known flank margin cave on Guam is Ritidian Cave. Entered through a very small hole (1m diam.), its single room (40m wide x 10m high) has a relatively undecorated ceiling, suggesting frequent breakdown. The floor, however, is covered by flowstone and huge stalagmites, and there is a freshwater pool with submerged speleothems and passages at the far end of the cave. Castro's Cave is similar, having one large, steeply sloping room, which is divided by flowstone walls, giving the impression of several rooms and passages. There is a freshwater pool at its south end.

⊠ **RITIDIAN AND CASTRO'S CAVES**
Ritidian Cave is located 950m east-southeast of Ritidian Pt., at a cliff base 360m inland from the beach. This is a NO ACCESS area of Guam National Wildlife Refuge. Questions about it can be directed to the U.S. Fish & Wildlife Service at 355.5096. Castro's Cave is 2.3km northwest of Mergagan Pt., at the cliff base, 400m from Castro's Beach. Permission must be obtained from the Castro family prior to any visits. [Map #3]

Ritidian Cliff Cave.

Tarague cliffline. Note the extensive cave development along a distinct horizon, which marks a former sea level.

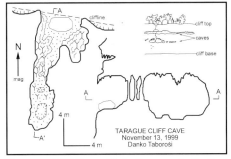

Tarague Cliff Cave. Note the cave's limited extent into the cliffline.

Tarague and Ritidian clifflines have many flank margin caves opened by a cliff retreat. Found at cliff bases and in cliff faces, they contain massive stalactites, grotesquely dissolved when the caves were flooded by former sea level highs.

◑ CAVES IN TARAGUE CLIFFS

Start at Tarague Beach and walk west along the shore. The large dome-shaped Mergagan Point Cave collapsed in an earthquake. About 100m farther is Tarague Cliff Cave. Its entrance is 15m up the cliff and can be entered by a careful free climb. There are more small caves at the base of the cliff, behind Tarague Beach. [Map #3]

◑ CAVES IN RITIDIAN CLIFFS

Ritidian Gate Cave is to the right of the Guam NWR main gate. Ritidian Beach Cave and Pictograph Cave are in the low cliffs behind the parking area and can be visited with U.S. Fish and Wildlife personnel. Ritidian Cliff Cave is in the cliff overlooking Ritidian Beach. Its huge 8mx20m entrance is visible from the parking area. For a great view of Ritidian, climb 10m up the cliff to this cave. [Map #2]

A pool in Asiga North Water Cave.

☒ ★ ASIGA WATER CAVES

Asiga Water Caves are extensive caves in the advanced stages of collapse. To reach them, start at Malojloj dump in Malojloj and walk down the cliff to Cool Cave (p. 51). From there, follow the cliffline south to a huge limestone boulder and a small man-made rock-pile wall. Traverse the sinkhole and some extremely jagged rock pinnacles to reach the large entrance of Asiga South Water Cave. The entrance is in a very large sinkhole at the base of a cliff, marked by numerous thick banyan tree roots. This cave is highly unstable and the roof in most passages is made of collapsed boulders and rubble. From this cave, go north-northeast across extremely rough terrain to reach a sinkhole containing the entrance to Asiga North Water Cave. You should wear gloves to avoid getting cut by the jagged limestone. Asiga North Water Cave is extremely difficult to find. Guam Boonie Stompers (653.2897) sometimes take their Saturday trips to these caves, so it is best to join them. Asiga area is rich in caves, so a careful search could result in discoveries of new ones. [Map #7]

☑ ⏰ YPAO CAVES

These caves are located in the Tamuning peninsula cliffs, about 2.5m above sea level. They have very large entrances and are filled with cemented beach sand and coral rubble. When tides are low and seas calm, start at Ypao Beach Park in Tumon and walk left (when facing the ocean) along the cliffline to the caves. At low tide, it may be possible to reach Agana Bay. [Map #1]

☒ GUMAYAS CAVES

The Gumayas Caves are located in the Togcha River Gorge (p. 27), near the stream, but hidden by vegetation. They are on the north side of the river, south of the narrowest part of the gorge. Look closely for faint trails or trail markers. The larger of the two caves, Gumayas Guma'Yu'us Cave, has a large domed room containing remnants of an altar. It was used as a church by the Chamorro population during WWII, and as a field hospital by the Imperial Japanese Army in late 1944. The second cave, Gumayas Chiget Cave, is located 46m downstream. It is a tubular, U-shaped passage, about 12m long. [Map #7]

☑ HILAAN WATER CAVES

There are two freshwater caves at the base of the cliff north of Lost Pond. Both are dominated by collapsed boulders and rubble. A collapse represents the natural demise of many caves, and the water caves at Hilaan are good examples of caves in this final stage. Their passages and rooms are defined by collapsed blocks, rather than bedrock. To get there, start at Lost Pond in Hilaan (p. 33) and walk north along a faint trail, following the base of the cliff. About 120m north of Lost Pond is the small entrance to Joan's Cave. This cave has rooms at different levels and leads to several small freshwater pools at the water table, about 12m down from the entrance. One of the pools is at least 3m deep and may lead to submerged passages. Hilaan Natural Well is 90m north of Joan's Cave, and has a very small entrance to the narrow passage leading 11m down to the freshwater level. The small pool is 1m² in area and about 6m deep. It appears to lead to submerged passages. There are several additional caves in the cliff behind Lost Pond. Search the area for new caves. [Map #1]

☒ TWEED'S CAVE

Tweed's Cave is not a cave, but an enlarged vertical fracture. It is where US Navy radioman George Tweed hid from the Japanese during WWII, from October 1942 until July 1944. See directions to Double Reef (p. 85). [Map #2]

☑ GADAO'S CAVE

Gadao's Cave is a small sea cave containing very famous ancient Chamorro pictographs. From Rt.4, go 1.3mi. east on Chagamin Lagu Ave., located on the north side of Inarajan Bay; turn right onto Chalan Guefan and continue 0.1mi. to a steep road on the right. Park, then walk to the beach, continuing 30m southeast along the coast to the cave. [Map #7]

☑ ASANITE CAVE

Asanite Cave is a large cave with a freshwater pool and extensive submerged passages, located at the base of a cliff and opened by a collapse. It is located in Ipan, on Rt.4, in the back yard of the house across from Asanite Cove (p. 88). As it is on private property, you must obtain permission from the owners before visiting this cave. [Map #7]

☒ FINDING NEW CAVES

With a basic understanding of the geology of Guam and the processes of cave development you can find many new or little-known caves. For example, stream caves develop along the surface contact between volcanic rock and limestone, so following and examining this boundary can result in new stream cave discoveries. The surface contact between limestone and volcanic terrain is recognized by differences in vegetation: limestone areas tend to be covered by forests; volcanic areas are usually grasslands or "red dirt." Special attention should be paid to the layout of valleys and ephemeral streams, because many caves are associated with the flow of water. Caves are also numerous in heavily fractured areas, because they commonly develop by enlargement of fractures. On coastal terraces, caves commonly open by roof collapse, and very large caves can have tiny entrances. If looking for caves, investigate even the smallest holes, as they may be enterances to large, specious caverns. The most likely places to find caves are volcanic-limestone contacts, fractured areas, coastal terraces, and cliffs.

Other Caves on Guam   61

SPRINGS

Fresh water from this small beach spring south of Ritidian emerges from underneath beach rock and can be noticed only during low tides.

Small sandy coves, such as this one between Ritidian and Tarague, are often locations of coastal springs and seeps.

5 cm (2 in)

Fresh water often emerges from fractures in coastal rocks. With time, freshwater flow may enlarge some of the fractures.

Springs are points where fresh water flows out of the ground. The water feeding the springs can originate from groundwater supply and/or direct rainwater input. If a spring has a constant flow rate, irrespective of weather conditions, it is probably fed by groundwater. If a spring has a relatively constant flow rate, but radically diminishes or disappears during the dry season, it is most likely fed by a small groundwater body. If a spring is flashy, which means that it increases its flow during and following rains, it is probably connected to the surface and receives direct rainwater input in addition to groundwater. There are two main types of springs on Guam: coastal springs, which are typical of islands, and discharge at sea level; and inland springs, also known as high level springs, which usually drain isolated limestone outcrops, located above the sea level. Coastal springs belong to several types: beach springs and seeps, seepage zones on reefs, fracture springs, cave springs, and submarine springs.

The beach in Tumon Bay has numerous freshwater springs and seeps, most of which can be seen only at low tide when they produce channels and rills in the sand. The largest springs discharge an estimated 15 mil. L per day. Photo below shows the springs in shallow water, bubbling up to the surface.

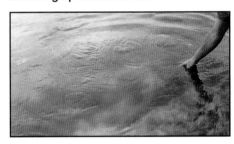

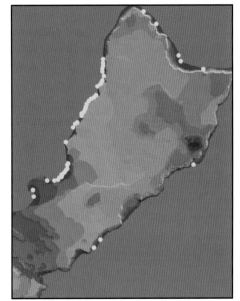

Locations of known coastal springs and seeps in northern Guam. The featured springs include beach springs and seeps, springs emerging from fractures and caves, and freshwater springs below the sea level. Beach springs are rare in southern Guam.

Fresh groundwater floats on salty groundwater, because of differences in density. The fresh groundwater body has the shape of a lens — it is thickest in the island's interior and thinnest along the coastline. As rainwater recharges the lens, fresh water in the lens moves toward the coastline, where it flows out from coastal springs. Such discharge is common on beaches and occurs as beach springs (point discharge) and seepage zones (diffuse discharge). They are best observed at low tides.

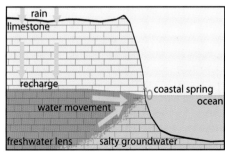

Groundwater moves toward the coast and discharges from coastal springs.

Beach Springs and Seeps   63

Fracture Springs

Scott's Fracture is a fracture in the coastal bench. It discharges a steady stream of fresh water into the ocean.

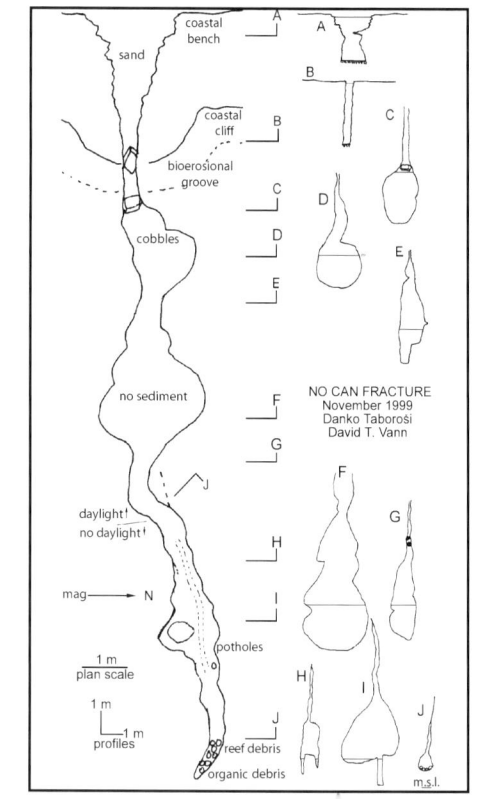

NO CAN FRACTURE
November 1999
Danko Taboroši
David T. Vann

Because beach springs are concealed by sand, the nature of conduits feeding coastal springs is better seen on rocky shorelines and coastal cliffs. In those areas, fresh water can be observed emerging from fractures in the rock. Water moves via fractures, because it is much easier than moving through the rock itself. Such fractures exist on a variety of scales, from less than a centimeter to several meters wide. They are widened by dissolution by the water that flows in them. The largest fractures are wide enough to be directly explored and look like mini-canyons carrying freshwater streams emerging from the cliffs. The freshwater streams float on underlying seawater and this can be observed by snorkeling inside the fractures. The mixing zone between the two waters is called the halocline, and appears cloudy. Some fracture springs in northern Guam discharge over 8 mil. L per day.

Map and cross-sections of No Can Fracture, the longest explored discharging fracture on Guam.

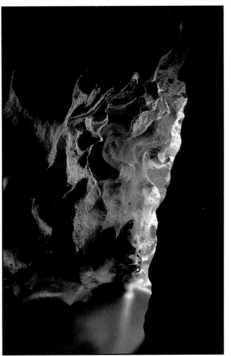

Map of Menpachi fracture, a very wide discharging fracture. Note "tributary" fractures contributing discharge.

Menpachi Fracture. Note the solutional sculpturing in the wall, created by water flowing in the fracture.

⊙⊕ FRACTURE SPRINGS

To find the most interesting fracture springs, start at Double Reef Beach (p. 85) and walk north along the coastal bench. This can be done only at low tide and during calm surf. The first large fracture you will encounter is Menpachi Fracture. A bit farther north is Scott's Fracture. Farther north is No Can Fracture, located about 30m south of a mushroom rock. Its entrance is tight and contains a wedged boulder. A mask and a flashlight are necessary for exploring this fracture. [Map #2]

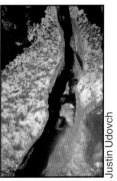

Exploring Scott's Fracture.

Justin Udovch

Fracture Springs

Submarine Springs

Braxton Plunkett

Because fresh groundwater floats on seawater in the ground, coastal springs typically discharge at sea level. However, freshwater can also discharge below the sea level from submarine fractures and caves, if there is enough pressure to push it. This can occur when old discharge pathways, formed when the sea level was lower, remain active. The deepest known submarine spring on Guam is located 11m below the sea level.

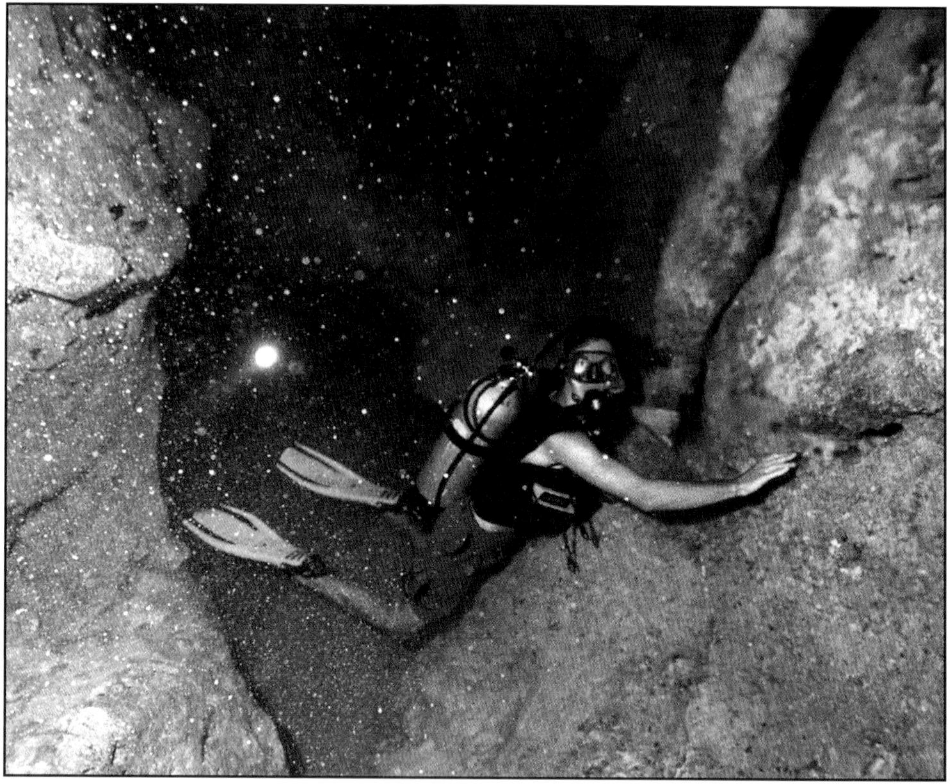

Matt's Freshwater Cave. A large submarine spring near Ague Cove. Water discharges from fractures in a cave at the base of a coastal cliff, at a depth of 11m.

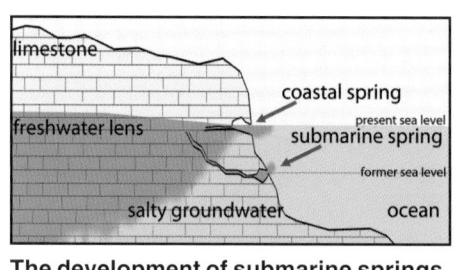

The development of submarine springs.

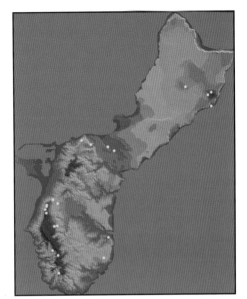

Locations of inland springs on Guam, most of which drain limestone areas surrounded by volcanic terrain. For exact locations see USGS topographic maps and GPS data provided on pp. 90-97.

Agana Springs stopped flowing after the installation of a GWA well 400m away.

Inland springs do not drain the NGLA. They are usually associated with smaller limestone outcrops, which sit on top of volcanic rock and contain perched groundwater; or with conduits, which form along the basement units and discharge water above the sea level (Janum Spring).

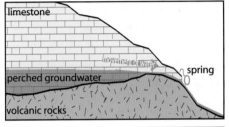

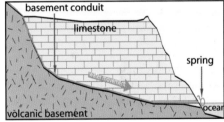

A typical high-level spring (top) and Janum Spring (bottom).

Inland Springs

PONDING BASINS AND WELLS

Although ponding basins and wells are not natural karst features, they are an important part of the freshwater cycle in northern Guam. Ponding basins and stormwater disposal wells are involved in aquifer recharge, while production wells are used for the extraction of water from the aquifer. Because northern Guam contains many densely populated areas and continues to rapidly develop, its natural landscape has been drastically modified. This includes the conversion of many natural depressions into stormwater ponding basins, and the building of culverts for urban runoff. Many ponding basins were originally karst sinkholes whose shape and appearance have been changed. Many ponding basins are thus natural points of recharge for the aquifer, and are therefore sensitive to pollution. Stormwater disposal wells are deep wells designed to quickly eliminate stormwater from the surface. These wells provide the most direct pathways for rainwater to reach the aquifer and are extremely sensitive to pollution.

A depression on Andersen Air Force Base, containing a cluster of 14 stormwater disposal wells.

An aerial view of a ponding basin in Dededo. The depression could be a natural sinkhole modified by urban development.

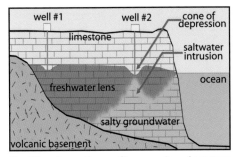

Profile of northern Guam, showing two production wells pumping water from the aquifer. Note the cones of depression. The cone of depression at well #2 has caused an upward coning of seawater, posing a contamination risk. Well #1, where freshwater is underlain by volcanic rock, is in no immediate danger.

Y-10, a GWA production well in Yigo.

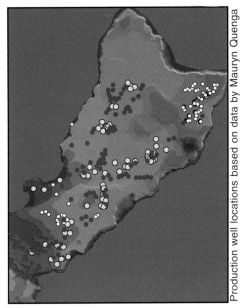

Locations of ponding basins (large circles), and injection wells (small circles); and the approximate locations of monitoring wells and production wells (blue dots) in northern Guam.

Over 80% of Guam's drinking water is obtained from the Northern Guam Lens Aquifer (NGLA). This water is extracted by production wells. The amount of water that can be safely extracted is limited, and is becoming a crucial issue as the population of Guam grows and the demand for fresh water increases. The NGLA is sensitive to overuse, because of its limited recharge (especially during droughts), and danger of saltwater intrusion (in cases of over-pumping). When water is pumped from a production well, it creates a cone of depression, a local lowering of the water table around the well. This causes the underlying seawater to cone upward, bringing salty water closer to the well. This is known as saltwater intrusion and is a serious danger to any island aquifer. Affected by saltwater intrusion, wells become contaminated by salt water for years — both the well that is causing the problem and the wells nearby. Wells used only to observe groundwater levels and water quality are known as monitoring wells.

Production and Monitoring Wells 69

Coastal zone karst is unique, because it is shaped by the ocean and marine organisms, in addition to fresh water. On Guam, it consists of a narrow coastal bench (just above the sea level) and an elevated reef terrace (several meters above the sea level). The coastal bench is within the intertidal zone and is home to algae and many marine organisms. It is commonly divided by low algal ridges into many shallow pools, which can be arranged in a step-like pattern, so that seawater pushed in by waves cascades over the ridges from one pool to another. The reef terrace is usually dominated by extremely jagged pits and pinnacles.

Solution basins in the coastal bench, south of Ague Cove. Above them are the jagged pinnacles of the elevated reef terrace.

Algal ridges and large, step-like pools on the coastal bench at Inarajan. Their origin is unclear and may be a result of algal growth, bioerosion, or dissolution.

Bioerosional grooves on the north end of Pago Bay are an obvious indicator of former higher sea level still stands.

Bioerosion is a process of erosion caused by living organisms. It is most intense in the intertidal zone, where it creates semi-circular bioerosional grooves, usually about 2m in diameter, cut into the coastal cliffs. These grooves are excellent sea level indicators. Those seen in the cliffs above the modern sea level were formed in the past, during higher stable sea levels. They are created by a variety of marine organisms, collectively known as bioeroders. On Guam, bioeroders include certain species of limpets, chitons, barnacles, and crabs. All of these erode limestone by grazing on algae living on the rock surface and in holes within the rock. Certain algae and bacteria are capable of boring into limestone and contribute to bioerosion. Bioerosion also occurs in deeper water, where it is carried out by a variety of grazing organisms, such as parrotfish and sea urchins.

Bioerosional grooves on small islands in Guma Fahou give these rocks the interesting "mushroom" shape.

Bioerosion

Beaches are coastal accumulations of sediment, usually sand. On Guam, they form in places protected from waves. They are well developed in areas along the west and north coast of Guam, where they are protected by fringing reefs. The northeast coast, however, having no protective reefs, has no beaches at all. This phenomenon is also easily observed on Cocos Island, whose lagoon side has a beautiful sandy beach, while its ocean side is composed of bare reef rock. The beach sand on Guam's limestone coastlines is calcareous — composed of tiny fragments of coral, algae, mollusks, and other organisms. In some places, like the Star Sand Beach Resort, the sand consists almost entirely of foraminifera — single-celled planktonic and benthic organisms whose shells can be shaped like little stars. Based on overall morphology, there are two beach types on Guam's limestone coastlines: linear beaches, such as Falcona and Ritidian, and embayment beaches, such as Tumon and Haputo (see photos).

Falcona Beach, a long linear beach, with beachrock deposits and calcareous sand.

Zonation on a typical Guam beach. Moving from the foreground toward the ocean, note the former uplifted reef (black) buried in calcareous sand (white), the consolidated sand known as beachrock (green), the modern lagoon, and the modern fringing reef front.

Aerial view of Haputo Beach, which has developed within an embayment. It looks like a small version of Tumon Bay.

Beachrock on Tarague Beach consists of consolidated and lithified beach sand.

☑ *BEACHES OF GUAM*

Starting in Hagåtña and going clockwise around the island, the beaches of northern Guam are Agana Bay, Tumon Bay, and Gun Beach (p. 77); Tanguisson Beach and Hilaan (p. 84) [Map #1]; Haputo Beach, Double Reef Beach, Falcona Beach, Uruno Beach, and Ritidian Beach (all on p. 85) [Map #2]; Jinapsan/Star Sand Beach, Tarague Beach, and a small cove near Tagua Point in the north [Map #3]. The east coast of northern Guam has no beaches, except for a few small coves in Janum and in Mangilao, north of Fadian Point (p. 86) [Map #6]. In southeastern Guam [Map #7], starting in Mangilao, there are Pago Bay Beach, Taga'chang Beach, Ipan Beach, Talofofo Bay and Paicpouc Cove (magnetite sand), Matala Beach, three small beaches in Asiga (all on p. 88); and Nomna Bay, Pauliluc Bay, Agfayan Bay, and Atao Beach. Other beaches in southern Guam are on volcanic terrain (Merizo, Umatac, and Agat). On the Orote Peninsula, south to north, are Dadi Beach, Tipalo Beach, Orote Channel Beach (p. 89), and Gab Gab.

Beaches

Most of the limestone coastline of Guam consists of cliffs, rising from 60m to 200m above sea level. This includes the entire coast of northern Guam, the eastern coast of southern Guam, and the southern coast of Orote Peninsula. The cliffs are actually ancient coral reefs, which turned into limestone when the island was elevated and the relative sea level dropped. Although shear cliffs are immediately adjacent to the ocean in places, most areas have local terraces extending from the cliff base to the waterline. Often, there are several such terraces arranged in a step-like pattern, indicating episodic changes in sea level. Clifflines are constantly attacked by wave erosion, which causes them to retreat landward by episodic collapses.

⌂ RAPPELLING COASTAL CLIFFS

Guam's coastal cliffs are exciting places to rappel and climb (by top rope). Taga'chang and the cliffs in Tamuning are excellent, because they can be quickly climbed for repeated rappelling. You must be properly trained in order to engage in rappelling.

Cliffs at Pati Point. Note the step-like pattern of cliff terraces, indicative of previous sea level stillstands.

Cliffline at Amantes (Two Lovers) Point.

The Orote Caverns, two large caves in Orote cliffline, opened by a cliff retreat (cliffline erosion by wave action).

Sea caves are not true karst caves, because they are not formed by dissolution but by physical erosion by waves. They develop in cliffs with structural weaknesses (e.g. fractures) and in direct contact with the waves. As waves crash into coastal cliffs, the zones of weakness erode more easily than the rest of the cliff, and develop sea caves. Sea caves are common on Guam, and it can be difficult to distinguish between them and true karst caves. Typically, the walls and ceilings of sea caves are blocky, showing evidence of wave pounding and collapse, with few, if any, dissolutional features. Most sea caves on Guam are located on the east coast of northern Guam, where the absence of fringing reefs and beaches means no protection from waves. Possibly, storm waves, as opposed to constant pounding of routine waves, are instrumental in the creation of sea caves, due to the enormous pressures they exert on the cliffs. Exploring sea caves is very dangerous and can be attempted only during absolutely calm seas.

Guam's northeast coast, unprotected by reefs, is almost constantly beaten by waves; therefore, a large number of sea caves have developed there. Photos show sea caves near Anao Point (left) and Lujuna Point (top).

Sea Caves

Reefs are modern carbonate deposits, built by living organisms in shallow water. They are found along the entire coastline of Guam, except in the northeast. Reefs adjacent to the coast are known as fringing reefs. On Guam, they range from narrow benches, formed by encrusting algae, to reef up to 800m wide, formed by a variety of corals and algae. The part of the reef breaking the waves is called the reef margin or reef front, while the back portion is called the reef flat. The reef margin is usually not created by corals but by *Porolithon* algae, which thrive in wave-agitated environments. They grow in a peculiar pattern known as spur-and-groove morphology, consisting of series of parallel ridges, 90° to the reef front, separated by deep grooves. In addition to the ubiquitous fringing reefs, Guam has small reefs discontinuous to the coast. They are known as patch reefs, and Double Reef is the best example. Finally, there are two barrier reefs on Guam: Cocos Reef, which fully encloses a large lagoon (7.5km²), and Luminao Reef, which partially encloses a small one.

Aerial view of Cocos Lagoon, its barrier reef, and Cocos Island — a barrier reef islet.

Aerial view of Pago Bay and its large fringing reef. Note the prominent channel in the reef, caused by freshwater discharge from Pago River.

John Jenson

Snorkeling in the beautiful Ague Cove, between Tanguisson and Haputo Beach.

Double Reef offers some of the nicest reefs on Guam and great visibility.

☑ AGANA AND TUMON BAYS

Rick's Reef (at the north end of Agana Bay, next to the Palace Hotel), Ypao Beach (at the south end of Tumon), and Gun Beach (at the north end of Tumon) are all great snorkeling spots. When conditions permit, so is the base of Amantes Point, reached in 30 minutes by walking north from Gun Beach. [Map #1]

☑🕐 TANGUISSON AND HILAAN

Tanguisson Beach has a nice fringing reef and offers good reef front snorkeling. To the north is Hilaan, and Shark's Hole, a 6.5m-deep depression. Despite its name, it has no sharks and is an easy snorkeling spot. Freshwater snorkeling in the nearby Lost Pond (p. 33) is also fun. [Map #1]

☒🕐 NORTHWEST COAST

Some of the most pristine fringing reefs on Guam are found in the northwest. Snorkeling is good anywhere, when conditions permit. The most accessible spots include Ague Cove (p. 84), Haputo Beach (p. 85), Double Reef (p. 85), and Uruno Beach (p. 85). Farther north is Ritidian, which is extremely dangerous due to strong ocean currents. [Map #2]

☒🕐 NORTHEAST COAST

The northeast is usually too rough for safe snorkeling. The bottom slopes steeply, water is rough and deep, and there are few reefs. Fadian Cove (p. 86) is a good place when it is not too rough. Pago Bay can be great, both on the reef flat and beyond the reef margin. The UOG Marine Lab provides good access. Snorkeling beyond the reef should be attempted only during calm seas. [Map #6]

☑🕐 SOUTHERN GUAM

Some great snorkeling sites in southern Guam include Cocos Lagoon, Sella Bay, Anae Island, Agat reefs, Gab-Gab and Orote Channel (on the Orote Peninsula), and Luminao Reef (at Glass Breakwater, in Apra Harbor). Cocos Lagoon and Anae Island are accessed by boat. You should carry a dive flag buoy.

☑ SALAGLULA POOLS

While not exactly snorkeling spots due to poor visibility, these "natural pools" are good examples of sinkholes flooded by sea level rise. They have limited ocean circulation and are popular swimming spots. [Map #7]

Guam has experienced dynamic sea level changes in the past, which has caused many karst features to become flooded. Since the minimum known sea level was 95m below the current one, karst caves and sinkholes probably exist down to that depth. Although now submarine, such features have all developed on dry land or in fresh groundwater. Karst features cannot develop in seawater, because it is saturated with respect to $CaCO_3$ and cannot cause its dissolution.

Braxton Plunkett

Matt's Cave is the deepest documented submarine cave on Guam. Its entrance depth is 50m; its lowest known point is at 65m; and its total length is over 200m. Caves like this could not have developed under the sea, but were probably created when the relative sea level was much lower than it is today.

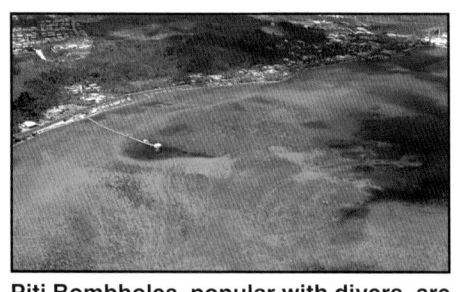

Piti Bombholes, popular with divers, are not actual bomb holes, but sinkholes that have been flooded by the rise in sea level.

One of Guam's favorite dive spots, Blue Hole, is a pit cave, much like the pit at Amantes Point (p. 19), but one that has been submerged by sea level rise.

Justin Udovch

★ BLUE HOLE

Blue Hole is a pit cave, submerged by the sea level rise. It is a vertical shaft in a fringing reef, starting at a depth of 20m. It extends to approximately 95m below sea level. At 42m, a large window in the outer wall provides a way for the diver to exit. Descending into Blue Hole is a fantastic experience and it is easy to lose track of time and depth. This dive is for experienced divers only, and access is by boat only. [Map #8]

★ THE CREVICE

The Crevice is a narrow fracture about 200m south of the Blue Hole. The upper part of the fracture is at a depth of approximately 30m, and its bottom depth ranges from 70m to 130m+ at the mouth. The fracture walls are vertical in places and gently sloping in others, and are covered by sea fans, soft corals and gorgonians. Access is by boat only. [Map #8]

☑ ANAE CAVERNS

Located on the south and north side of Anae Island in Agat, these caverns are easy dives, requiring no cave diving experience. Depth reaches 10m. Access is by boat. [Map #8]

☑ PITI BOMBHOLES

Despite their name, Piti Bombholes are natural sinkholes, submerged by a sea level rise. They were not made by bombs. Up to 10m deep, they are home to fish quite used to divers. The Fisheye Observatory was built in the deepest hole. Start at the beach opposite MDA in Piti and swim out 70m along the Fisheye access bridge.

★ NORTHERN CAVES

In some of Guam's most spectacular water caves, divers can enter through an entrance in the ocean and then follow the cave passages inland, rising through the halocline into the freshwater pools and inland caves with exits into the jungle. Pagat and Haputo areas contain such caves, but for safety reasons, their locations cannot be published. Contact a local dive shop for information.

☑ TOUGAN, BILE, FOUHA BAYS

These bays have spectacular reef caves (pseudokarst) at their reef fronts, at depths of 3m-20m. All are accessible from the beach by swimming out to the reef. Tougan and Bile are in Merizo; Fouha is in Umatac. [Map #8]

There are about 22 fringing islets around Guam. Cocos is the largest, with an area of 0.38km². Others range from less than 1000m² (Camel Rock and Noddy Island) to over 30,000 m² (Neye, Orote, and Anae islands). Most are small islets on fringing reef flats (Asgadao, Fotos, Guijen, etc.); two are off reef (Anae, Camel Rock); and two are barrier reef islands (Cocos, Babe). Most are less than 10m in elevation, but a few are taller: Orote (43m), Facpi (26m), Neye (23m), and Alupat (14m). The distance between the islets and Guam ranges between 2.5m (Orote Channel islets) and 2.5km (Cocos Island).

Anae Island, off Agat, is an extremely eroded limestone islet with several caves and a small cave pool.

Facpi Island, just off Facpi Point, is the only islet around Guam that is not made entirely of limestone. A clear contact between black volcanic rocks and overlying limestone can be seen on the island. One can walk to Facpi at low tide, over a flat stretch of basalt.

Kayaking around Anae Island, Agat.

🕐① ★ OROTE ISLAND & CLIFFS

From Family Beach on Glass Breakwater, kayak across Apra Harbor to Orote Point. There is a beautiful small lagoon nestled between the tip of the peninsula and Orote Island. If the sea is not rough, you can continue kayaking south along the spectacular Orote cliffline, but there are no landings until Agat, almost 10km away (allow at least 3 hours). [Map #8]

🕐① ★ ANAE & FACPI ISLANDS

Start from the beach south of Agat Marina and head toward Anae Island. To avoid the breaking waves at Anae Reef, the best way to reach the island is to approach it from the north and go counterclockwise around it to a calm area in the southeast. For an extended trip, go to Facpi Island and points farther south. There are no landing spots with car access until you reach Umatac. [Map #8]

☑ COCOS ISLAND & LAGOON

Kayaking from Merizo to Cocos Island is a great way to explore and snorkel in Cocos Lagoon. You can also visit the small and barren island of Babe, east of Cocos Island. To be safe, always stay inside the lagoon.

🕐① ★ ALUPAT ISLAND

Start in Agana Bay and kayak around the beautiful Alupat Island in the north part of the bay. If the sea is not rough, you can kayak to Tumon Bay, along Tamuning cliffs. [Map #1]

🕐 ★ NORTHWEST COAST

Start at Gun Beach or Tanguisson and kayak north to Hilaan, Haputo, or even Double Reef. Allow time to return. Attempt only during very calm seas. [Maps #1, #2]

🕐 ★ PAGO BAY & MANGILAO

Pago Bay has a large fringing reef, which is great for kayaking. Start at the Francisco P. Perez picnic area or the UOG Marine Lab. Venturing outside the reef can be done only on very calm days, when you can kayak north along the cliffline. There are no landing spots, so you must return to where you started. Heading south, the nearest landing with car access is in Ylig Bay. [Map #6]

☑ SOUTHERN RIVERS

Ylig, Talofofo, and Inarajan rivers can be kayaked quite a distance upstream. Start at Ylig, Talofofo, or Inarajan bays. [Map #7]

Sea Kayaking Trips 81

Hikers on the cliffs in Malojloj, looking over the wild and rugged Asiga coastline.

Hiking is a great way to explore the beauty of Guam. While karst areas provide some of the island's most spectacular landscapes, they also impose special demands on hikers: rugged terrain, jagged and slippery limestone, absence of trails, dense brush, lack of fresh water, etc. Nearly all of the treks described on the following pages are very difficult. Even the shortest ones will take several hours, and most require an entire day with an early start. The coastal treks are along rugged coastlines, isolated by soaring cliffs, having few, if any, vehicle access points or actual trails. You will often be exposed to waves and may need to swim short distances. Many treks are one-way and need to be planned in advance. Always carry topo maps; know the weather and tide conditions; know in advance the trails by which you plan to leave the coastline; and leave vehicles at appropriate locations. If you have no hiking experience on Guam, you should first go on boonie stomps, organized each Saturday (call 653.2897 for information).

⊠ MT. LAMLAM

Mt. Lamlam (406m) is the tallest peak on Guam and the southernmost peak on a limestone ridge, which also includes Mt. Alifan, Mt. Taene, and Mt. Almagosa. The ridge sits on a volcanic base and grew as a coral reef 8-5 million years ago. Land uplift and a sea level drop caused the reef to become exposed as high ground. Coral and other fossils are easy to find on Mt. Lamlam. The trail begins at a ranch across from Cetti Bay Overlook on Rt.2, about 4mi. south of Agat. You start on volcanic terrain, but will soon notice the abrupt change in vegetation as you reach the limestone. The first limestone outcrop you encounter contains a Catholic shrine in a shelter cave. The trail branches at the top of the ridge, leading to Mt. Jumullong Manglo (with metal crosses at the top) on the right, and to Mt. Lamlam on the left. The Mt. Lamlam trail proceeds north and enters a grassland and forest area and is difficult to follow. With some luck, you will reach a knoll with a concrete platform and a stick at the top. It is marked by a USGS metal marker (Mt. Lamlam — 1,311ft). The true peak (406m/ 1,332ft) can be seen farther north. [Map #8]

⊠ SOUTHERN SPRINGS

All rainfall on the Mt. Alifan to Mt. Lamlam ridge percolates into limestone. It accumulates as groundwater, and flows under the limestone on volcanic rock, emerging at the land surface in places where the limestone terrain ends and volcanic terrain begins. Almagosa, Dobo, Chepak and Bona springs flow on the east side of the ridge and are within the Naval Magazine; Santa Rita Spring, developed by GWA, flows on the north side; Faata, Auau, and Mao springs flow on the west slopes of the ridge, in the wild mountain terrain south of Agat. To try to reach Faata, Auau, and Mao springs, use the maps and GPS coordinates provided [Map #8], as there are no trails. Although the springs are very hard to find and are often all but dry, the terrain is spectacular, contains many WWII artifacts, and offers great views. In the mountains of southern Guam, there are additional springs — Alatgue, Piga, and Siligin — flowing out of small bodies of Maemong limestone on the steep volcanic slopes. All are ephemeral and hard to find. There is a hiking trail to Siligin Spring along the Geus River, from Merizo to Mt. Finasantos. Use a topographic map and the GPS coordinates provided on p. 97.

Limestone ridge overlooking Agat. The grasslands are on volcanic terrain; the forests are on limestone. This ridge was deposited as a coral reef and perfectly illustrates the dramatic sea level changes Guam has experienced.

⊠ OTHER LIMESTONE PEAKS

Start south of Agat and head east, up the volcanic slopes, covered in swordgrass, and the limestone terrain, covered by dense brush. This is extremely difficult terrain, with few or no trails. To reach Mt. Taene, a limestone peak overlooking Agat, start at Rt.2 and turn onto Umang Road, 1mi. south of Agat Cemetery, and continue to the end. Alternatively, park at the VFW (Veterans of Foreign Wars) Club in Agat and walk along the dirt road; then make your own trail. [Map #8]

Limestone Highlands

The coastline south of Tanguisson.

☉⊕ GUN BEACH TO TANGUISSON

This coastal hike can be done only during low tides and calm seas. From Rt.1, take the road to Two Lovers Point and drive to Tanguisson Beach, where you should drop off one vehicle. Start your hike at the opposite end, at Gun Beach, behind the Nikko Hotel in Tumon. Walk north through the shallow water around Bijia Point, to Fafai Beach. Latte stones are found in the forest inland from the beach; Fafai Cave is in the clifline behind it (p. 55). Farther north, you can walk around the base of Amantes Point. Continue north to Tanguisson, over jagged coastal rocks containing many coral fossils. [Map #1]

☉ TANGUISSON TO HILAAN

Starting from Rt.1, across from Micronesia Mall, follow the road to Two Lovers Point and proceed to Tanguisson Beach. Park there and walk north along the coast to Guma Fahou and its interesting mushroom rock islands, created by bioerosion. Continue north, along two sandy beaches, separated by rocky headlands, to the beautiful Hilaan Beach. There you will find a snorkeling spot at Shark's Hole (p. 77), a sinkhole pool at the Lost Pond (p. 33), and several caves (p. 61). [Map #1]

⊗⊕① HILAAN TO AGUE

You can reach Ague Cove in approximately 4 hours by proceeding north from Hilaan; but the trek is extremely difficult — partly on the coastal reef bench and partly over jagged coastal limestone. Therefore, it should be attempted only during low tide and a very calm sea. Because rising tides prevent making a round trip, you must be familiar with the trail out at Ague Cove (see next column) and have a vehicle waiting there. [Map #1]

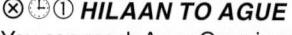

A limestone outcrop on Uruno Beach, bearing marks of former sea levels.

☒ AGUE COVE

From the intersection of Rt.1 and Rt.3 in Dededo, follow Rt.3 north for 2.7mi.; then turn left and continue bearing right until you reach the end of the road at the abandoned Oceanview housing area. The trail starts there and heads west, down the steep cliff to Ague Cove. Snorkeling is great, but the water can be cold due to the freshwater springs. You can explore the coastline south to Hilaan (see previous column), or north to Haputo (p. 85), but the treks are extremely difficult, take a long time, and can be attempted only during low tide and very calm seas. They must be planned carefully, and you must know by which trail you plan to return to "civilization." [Map #2]

☑ HAPUTO BEACH

The pristine Haputo Beach is a quiet sandy embayment on the rugged northwestern coast. It is on U.S. Navy property and has been designated Haputo Ecological Reserve Area (call 339.5208 for more information). To reach Haputo, drive through the main gate of the Naval Computer & Telecommunications Station at Finagayan, which requires base access; then turn left at the first road and drive 1mi. to the trailhead, where you can park. The trail to the beach is steep and partially covered by concrete steps. There are latte stones in the forest, and a cave at the north end of the beach. [Map #2]

The rugged coastline north of Hilaan.

☒ DOUBLE REEF

Double Reef is one of the most pristine coastal areas on Guam. It is accessible by trail from the Naval Computer & Telecommunications Station (Finagayan), so base access is required. After entering the main gate, turn left at the first road and continue 1.5 mi. to a dirt road entering from the right. Park there and follow the dirt road along several switchbacks until the road levels off and you see a steep trail on the right-hand side leading into the forest. The trail goes through the forest and over jagged limestone rocks. It is difficult to follow, so look for survey tape markers. You will pass a shallow sinkhole and a small freshwater puddle on the left. From there, a side trail branches off to the right and goes over limestone boulders to the cliff, where you will find Tweed's Cave (p. 61). The main trail continues north, passes the entrance to Frankie's Cave (p. 56) on the right, and reaches Double Reef Beach. The snorkeling there is great. During low tides and calm seas, you can go south to Coconut Crab Cave (p. 57), and north to spectacular fracture springs (pp. 64-65), and farther to Uruno and Ritidian. [Map #2]

⊗ ⏱ ① DOUBLE REEF TO RITIDIAN

You can walk from Double Reef Beach north to Uruno only during low tides and very calm seas. Follow the coastal bench past several tiny coves, spectacular fractures discharging fresh water (pp. 64-65), and a natural arch (see front cover photo). You will then reach Kakanu Cave, a large sea cave at the south end of Falcona Beach. The rocks there are not a raised reef, but lithified beach sand, known as beachrock. Farther north are South Uruno Cave and the long, linear Uruno Beach. You will pass a large limestone outcrop containing several caves, formed during former higher sea levels (photo on p. 84). Farther north is Ritidian, where you should have a vehicle waiting. Do not stray inland at Uruno unless you have permission from the Artero family, who own the land. [Map #2]

⊙ RITIDIAN TO URUNO BEACH

From junction with Rt.9, proceed north on Rt.3, to its end at Ritidian. Park there and walk south along the coast to Uruno Beach. Double Reef (see box above) can also be reached if the tide is low and the sea is calm. Guam NWR (Ritidian) gate closes at 5PM. [Map #2]

A geologic fault extending from Mt. Santa Rosa and intersecting the coastal cliffline at Mati Point.

⊗ FADIAN POINT

Start at the Fadian Fish Hatchery (p. 54). Walk out to the ocean and explore along the rugged limestone coastline. Fadian Point and Cove are to the north; Iates Point is to the south. [Map #6]

☑ FADIAN COVE

Fadian Cove is a beautiful small cove nestled in the rugged northeastern coastline. To reach the trailhead, go north on Rt.15 from Mangilao and, after passing the Methodist Church, turn right on Ignacio Way. Park at the end of the road and continue on foot. Stay left as you pass the old Fadian Quarry, until you reach a cliffline overlook, then follow the steep trail down to Fadian Cove. The Really Lost Pond (p. 33) is to the north of the cove. [Map #6]

⊗ ⊕ TAGUAN COASTLINE

Drive north on Rt.15, then turn right onto the road at the north edge of Mangilao Golf Course. Park at the end of the road and descend to the coast, using a stairway built through the limestone forest. Once at the coast, you can explore south to Taguan Cave and Fadian, or north to Taguan Point. [Map #6]

☉ CAMPANAYA POINT

To explore the coastline, follow the short trail from Marbo Cave (p. 53) to the coast. [Map #5]

⊗ PAGAT COASTLINE

To reach the remote Pagat coastline, follow the trail to Pagat Cave (p. 52) and continue to the coast. Explore north to Pagat Natural Arch and Pagat Point, and south to Campanaya Point and Marbo Cave (p. 53). Make sure you can recognize the trail back. [Map #5]

☉ JANUM (HANOM) COASTLINE

With permission from the Taitano family, you can drive from East Gayinero Rd. down their private road to the Janum coastline. [Map #4]

⊗ ANAO COASTLINE

Anao is one of the most pristine parts of Guam's coast. From the intersection of Rt.15 and Rt.10, drive 11.4 mi. north on Rt.15. Alternatively, go .3 mi. south from the back gate to AAFB. Turn east at the green concrete bus stop; turn right at the 2nd road; turn left after 0.2 mi.; then proceed 1.5 mi. Park at the clearing, check in with the local residents, and walk down the steep trail to Anao. This trail is very difficult to follow. [Map #4]

Pagat Natural Arch, formed by the partial collapse of a sea cave roof.

⊗ ⏱ ① PAGO BAY

The coastline of Pago Bay, south of the UOG Marine Lab, provides a nice walk along a beach full of fossilized corals. During very low tides and extremely calm seas, you can also walk/swim north from the Marine Lab, along the coast to Fadian. From there you can hike out to Rt.15 (see p. 86 for trail). Be well acquainted with the trail out and have a vehicle waiting for you, because the rising tides make a round trip impossible. [Map #6]

⊗ ⏱ ① TAGUAN TO CAMPANAYA

From Taguan (p. 86), walk north around Taguan Point and along the coast of the Sasajyan embayment to Campanaya Point, where there is vehicle access at Marbo Cave (p. 53). Make sure you can recognize the place you will end your trek and the trail to Marbo Cave, where you should have a parked car waiting. [Map #5]

⊗ ① CAMPANAYA TO PAGAT

You can walk from Campanaya Point/Marbo Cave north to the Pagat coastline, although the terrain is extremely rough, with no trails. If you know the trail out from Pagat coast to Rt.15 via Pagat Cave (p. 52) and have a car waiting, you can leave that way. Otherwise, backtrack to Marbo Cave. [Map #5]

⊗ ⏱ NORTH FROM ANAO

The trail to Anao is one of the few trails providing access to the rugged northeastern coast. To explore this spectacular area, hike down the Anao trail (p. 86) and continue north along the coast. You will discover interesting sea caves, and amazing scenery. Make sure you can recognize the trail back. [Map #4]

⊗ ⏱ SOUTH FROM ANAO

Starting at Anao (p. 86), hike south to explore the rugged and remote coastline. There are no trails; follow the coastline. Mati Point is about 1.5km away. Farther south is the Janum coast, with a few beaches and many small caves. This area is private property and permission is needed from the Taitano family if you plan to wander inland. Farther south, north of Lujuna Point, is Janum Spring, where a once traversable cave was destroyed in the 1993 earthquake. [Map #4]

A spectacular double sea arch and a collapsed roof are remnants of a cave at Lafac Point.

⊗🕐① PAGO TO TAGA'CHANG

For a glimpse of the extremely rugged southeastern coastline, take one of the dirt roads just south of the Pago River Bridge to the south side of Pago Bay. From there, walk south along the coastline if the tide is low and the sea very calm. Passing around Pago Point and Ricky's Beach, you will reach Taga'chang Beach, where you should have a car waiting. To reach Taga'chang by car, from Pago River Bridge, drive south on Rt.4 to the top of the hill and take the steep road on the left. [Map #7]

☑ RICKY'S BEACH

To get to Ricky's Beach from Rt.4, take the turnoff to Taga'chang Beach (see above) and park 0.2mi. down the road. Walk southeast along the dirt road to the trail leading down the cliff to Ricky's Beach. [Map #7]

⊗🕐① TAGA'CHANG TO YLIG

Beginning at Taga'chang Beach (see above), follow the rugged coastline south to Ylig Bay. Before reaching the north side of Ylig Bay, take a dirt road back to Rt.4 to avoid swampy vegetation at Ylig Bay. You should have a car waiting at the Ylig Bay Bridge. [Map #7]

☉🕐① YLIG TO TALOFOFO BAY

For a long relaxing walk along Ipan Beach, start at Ylig Point/Togcha Cemetery (located south of the junction of Rt.4 and Rt.17, on the east side of Rt.4). Walk south to Ipan Beach Park, Asanite Cove, or Talofofo Bay. For a one-way hike, drop off a vehicle at any of these points. The sandy beach ends north of Asanite; the rest is difficult rocky shoreline. [Map #7]

⊠ ASIGA COASTLINE

To reach the spectacular Asiga coastline, take a trail down Malojloj cliff (see directions to Cool Cave, p. 51). From the cave, rough out your own trail to the coast, making sure you can find the way back. Alternatively, make this a one-way hike south to Perez Beach, from where you can take a dirt road back to Rt.4. You should have a vehicle waiting. [Map #7]

⊗🕐① TALOFOFO TO ASIGA

The Asiga coastline can also be reached by taking a long coastal hike south from Talofofo Bay, via the black sand (magnetite) Paicpouc Cove and around Matala Point. [Map #7]

Asiga, as seen from Malojloj cliffs.

Hiking in Asiga limestone forest, over extremely rugged pinnacle karst.

☉⊕🕐① INARAJAN BAY

Several short interesting hikes can be taken along the rugged limestone coastline north and south of Inarajan Bay. Park anywhere in Inarajan. Beginning on the south side of the bay, walk along the coast to Salaglula Pools — two sinkholes with saltwater pools (p. 77). Beginning on the north side of the bay, proceed north along the coastline, passing Gadao's Cave (p. 61) to reach the Pauliluc Bay. By crossing the Pauliluc River, you can proceed farther north to the Nomna area (Perez Beach), Jalaihai Point, and the rugged Asiga coastline. Allow enough time to get back and try only when the ocean is calm. [Map #7]

☉ BEAR ROCK AND SOUTH

Bear Rock is a large limestone boulder on the south side of Agfayan Bay. To explore the area to the south of it, park on the south side of the bay, making sure to obtain permission from the local residents before proceeding. As you follow the coast south, the limestone terrain ends and volcanic terrain begins. [Map #7]

Aerial view of the pristine and secluded Orote Point, Orote Island and Channel.

☑ OROTE POINT / SPANISH STEPS

The beautiful tip of the Orote Peninsula, with its channel lagoon, rock islands, soaring cliffs, and seabird colonies, is one of the most serene places on Guam's coastline. At the base of the cliff is Orote Pond, a sinkhole at sea level, with dark brackish water. To reach this area, drive through the ComNavMarianas gate, at the south end of Rt.1. You must have base access or call 339.5208 for information. When Rt.1 ends, turn onto Orote Point Road and drive to the end for a spectacular view of the area below. Then drive back to the parking area on the north side of the road and continue on foot, down the ladder and the steep Spanish Steps to the bottom. [Map #8]

N

1 Km
1 Mi

	Lat. (N)	Long. (E)
GUN BEACH TO TANGUISSON		
a Gun Beach trailhead	13° 31.500'	144° 48.249'
1 Fafai Cave	13° 31.713'	144° 48.247'
TANGUISSON TO HILAAN		
b Tanguisson Beach	13° 32.640'	144° 48.569'
2 Guma Fahou	13° 32.910'	144° 48.658'
3 Shark's Hole	13° 33.463'	144° 48.959'
4 Lost Pond	13° 33.364'	144° 49.037'
HILAAN WATER CAVES		
5 Joan's Cave	13° 33.414'	144° 49.051'
6 Hilaan Natural Well	13° 33.458'	144° 49.066'
YPAO CAVES		
7 Ypao Cave 1		
8 Ypao Cave 2		
DEVIL'S PUNCHBOWL		
d Hilton parking area	13° 30.296'	144° 47.113'
9 Devil's Punchbowl	13° 30.155'	144° 47.141'
HARMON SINK		
e Mai'ana Hotel	13° 29.573'	144° 47.868'
10 Harmon Sink	13° 29.808'	144° 47.809'
OTHER SITES		
8 Amantes Pit Cave	13° 32.115'	144° 48.150'
11 Rick's Reef	north Agana Bay	
12 Alupat Island	north Agana Bay	
13 Ypao Beach	south Tumon Bay	

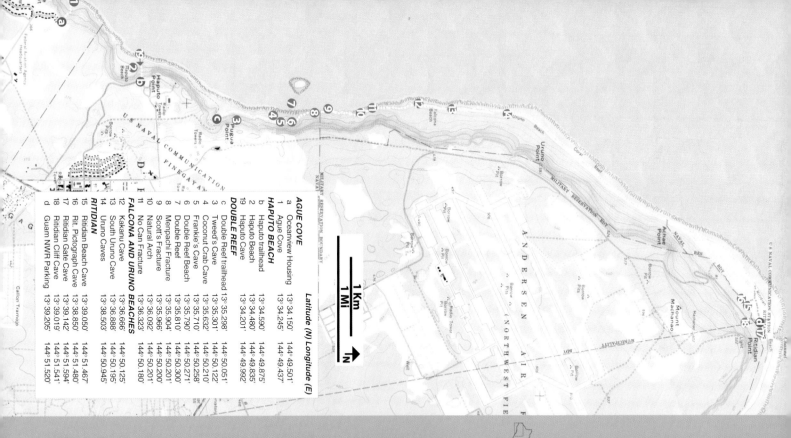

Latitude (N) Longitude (E)

AGUE COVE
		Latitude (N)	Longitude (E)
a	Oceanview Housing	13°34.150'	144°49.501'
1	Ague Cove	13°34.245'	144°49.437'

HAPUTO BEACH
b	Haputo trailhead	13°34.590'	144°49.875'
2	Haputo Beach	13°34.480'	144°49.835'
19	Haputo Cave	13°34.201'	144°49.992'

DOUBLE REEF
c	Double Reef trailhead	13°35.298'	144°50.051'
3	Tweed's Cave	13°35.301'	144°50.122'
4	Coconut Crab Cave	13°35.632'	144°50.210'
5	Frankie's Cave	13°35.710'	144°50.258'
6	Double Reef Beach	13°35.790'	144°50.271'
7	Double Reef	13°35.810'	144°50.300'
8	Menpachi Fracture	13°35.904'	144°50.201'
9	Scott's Fracture	13°35.966'	144°50.200'
10	Natural Arch	13°36.092'	144°50.201'
11	No Can Fracture	13°36.323'	144°50.180'

FALCONA AND URUNO BEACHES
12	Kakanu Cave	13°36.666'	144°50.125'
13	South Uruno Cave	13°36.888'	144°50.195'
14	Uruno Caves	13°38.503'	144°50.945'

RITIDIAN
15	Ritidian Beach Cave	13°39.050'	144°51.467'
16	Rit. Pictograph Cave	13°38.850'	144°51.480'
17	Ritidian Gate Cave	13°39.142'	144°51.594'
18	Ritidian Cliff Cave	13°39.019'	144°51.541'
d	Guam NWR Parking	13°39.205'	144°51.520'

1 Km
1 Mi

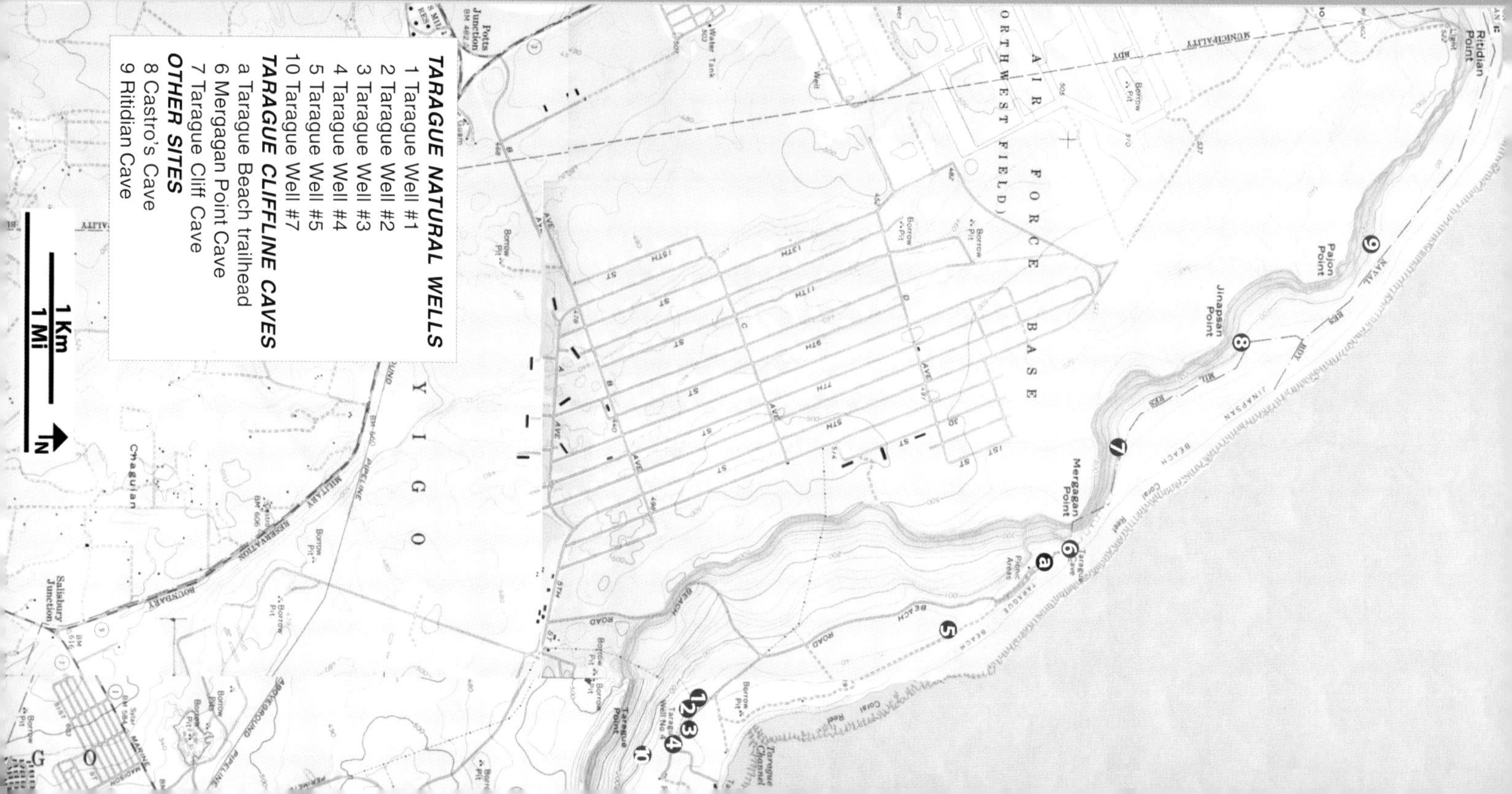

TARAGUE NATURAL WELLS
1 Tarague Well #1
2 Tarague Well #2
3 Tarague Well #3
4 Tarague Well #4
5 Tarague Well #5
10 Tarague Well #7

TARAGUE CLIFFLINE CAVES
a Tarague Beach trailhead
6 Mergagan Point Cave
7 Tarague Cliff Cave

OTHER SITES
8 Castro's Cave
9 Ritidian Cave

N

1 Km
1 Mi

AIR FORCE BASE
NORTHWEST FIELD

YIGO

Ritidian Point
Pajon Point
Jinapsan Point
Mergagan Point
Tarague Point
Tarague Channel

JINAPSAN BEACH
TARAGUE BEACH
BEACH ROAD

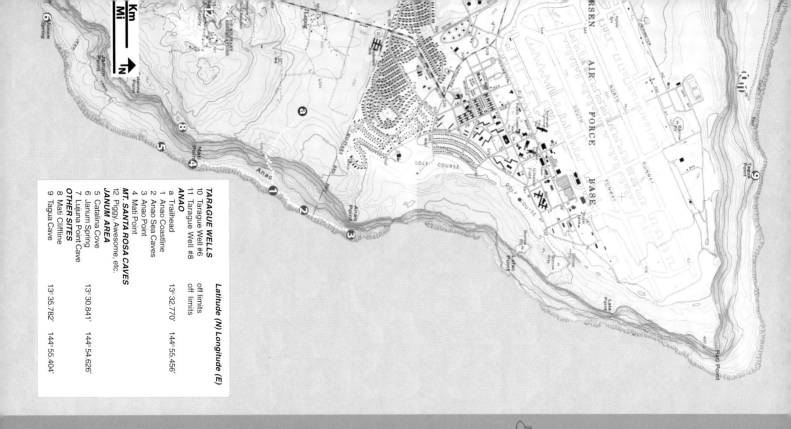

		Latitude (N) Longitude (E)
TARAGUE WELLS		
10 Tarague Well #6	off limits	
11 Tarague Well #8	off limits	
ANAO		
a Trailhead	13°32.770'	144°55.456'
1 Anao Coastline		
2 Anao Sea Caves		
3 Anao Point		
4 Mati Point		
MT. SANTA ROSA CAVES		
12 Piggy, Awesome, etc.		
JANUM AREA		
5 Catalina Cove		
6 Janum Spring	13°30.841'	144°54.626'
7 Lujuna Point Cave		
OTHER SITES		
8 Mati Cliffline		
9 Tagua Cave	13°35.782'	144°55.404'

Map 4: Northeastern Coastline

Tarague to Lujuna

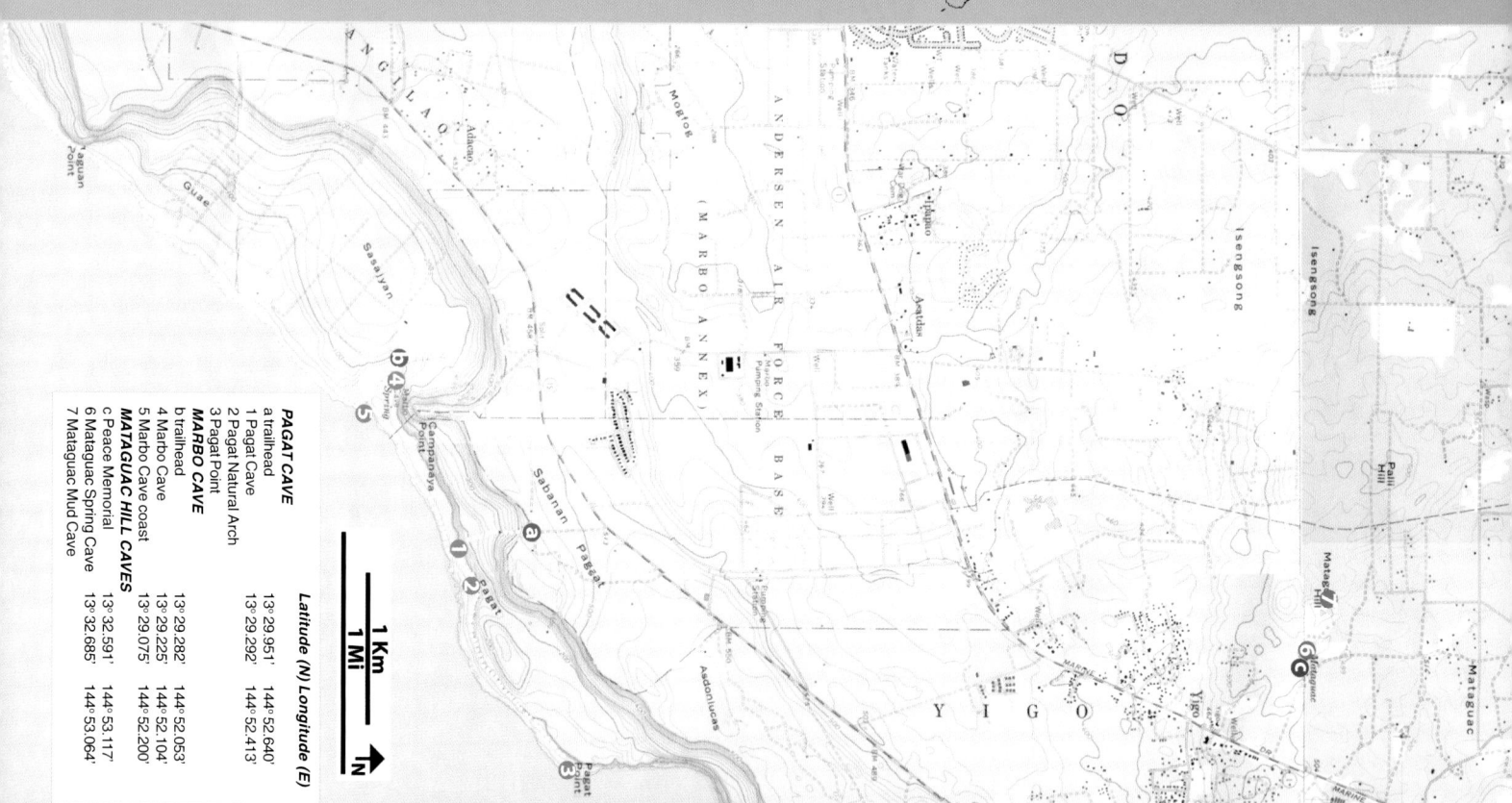

PAGAT CAVE

		Latitude (N)	Longitude (E)
a	trailhead	13° 29.951'	144° 52.640'
1	Pagat Cave	13° 29.292'	144° 52.413'
2	Pagat Natural Arch		
3	Pagat Point		
MARBO CAVE			
b	trailhead	13° 29.282'	144° 52.053'
4	Marbo Cave	13° 29.225'	144° 52.104'
5	Marbo Cave coast	13° 29.075'	144° 52.200'
MATAGUAC HILL CAVES			
c	Peace Memorial		
6	Mataguac Spring Cave	13° 32.591'	144° 53.117'
7	Mataguac Mud Cave	13° 32.685'	144° 53.064'

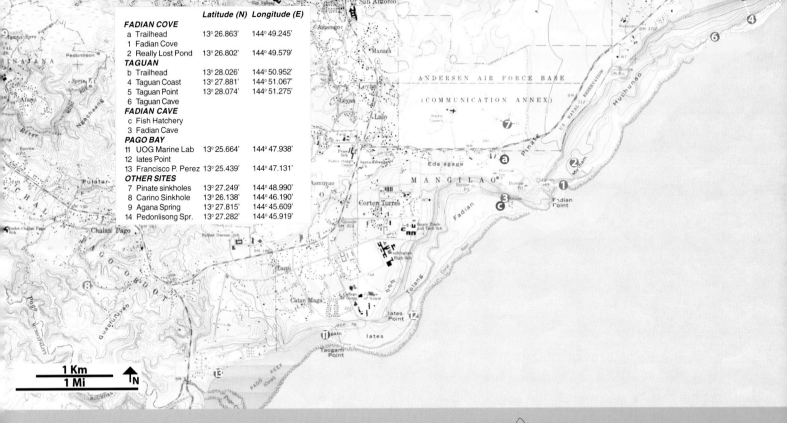

	Latitude (N)	Longitude (E)
FADIAN COVE		
a Trailhead	13° 26.863'	144° 49.245'
1 Fadian Cove		
2 Really Lost Pond	13° 26.802'	144° 49.579'
TAGUAN		
b Trailhead	13° 28.026'	144° 50.952'
4 Taguan Coast	13° 27.881'	144° 51.067'
5 Taguan Point	13° 28.074'	144° 51.275'
6 Taguan Cave		
FADIAN CAVE		
c Fish Hatchery		
3 Fadian Cave		
PAGO BAY		
11 UOG Marine Lab	13° 25.664'	144° 47.938'
12 Iates Point		
13 Francisco P. Perez	13° 25.439'	144° 47.131'
OTHER SITES		
7 Pinate sinkholes	13° 27.249'	144° 48.990'
8 Carino Sinkhole	13° 26.138'	144° 46.190'
9 Agana Spring	13° 27.815'	144° 45.609'
14 Pedonlisong Spr.	13° 27.282'	144° 45.919'

1 Km
1 Mi
N

Map 6: Northeastern Coastline Taguan to Pago **95**

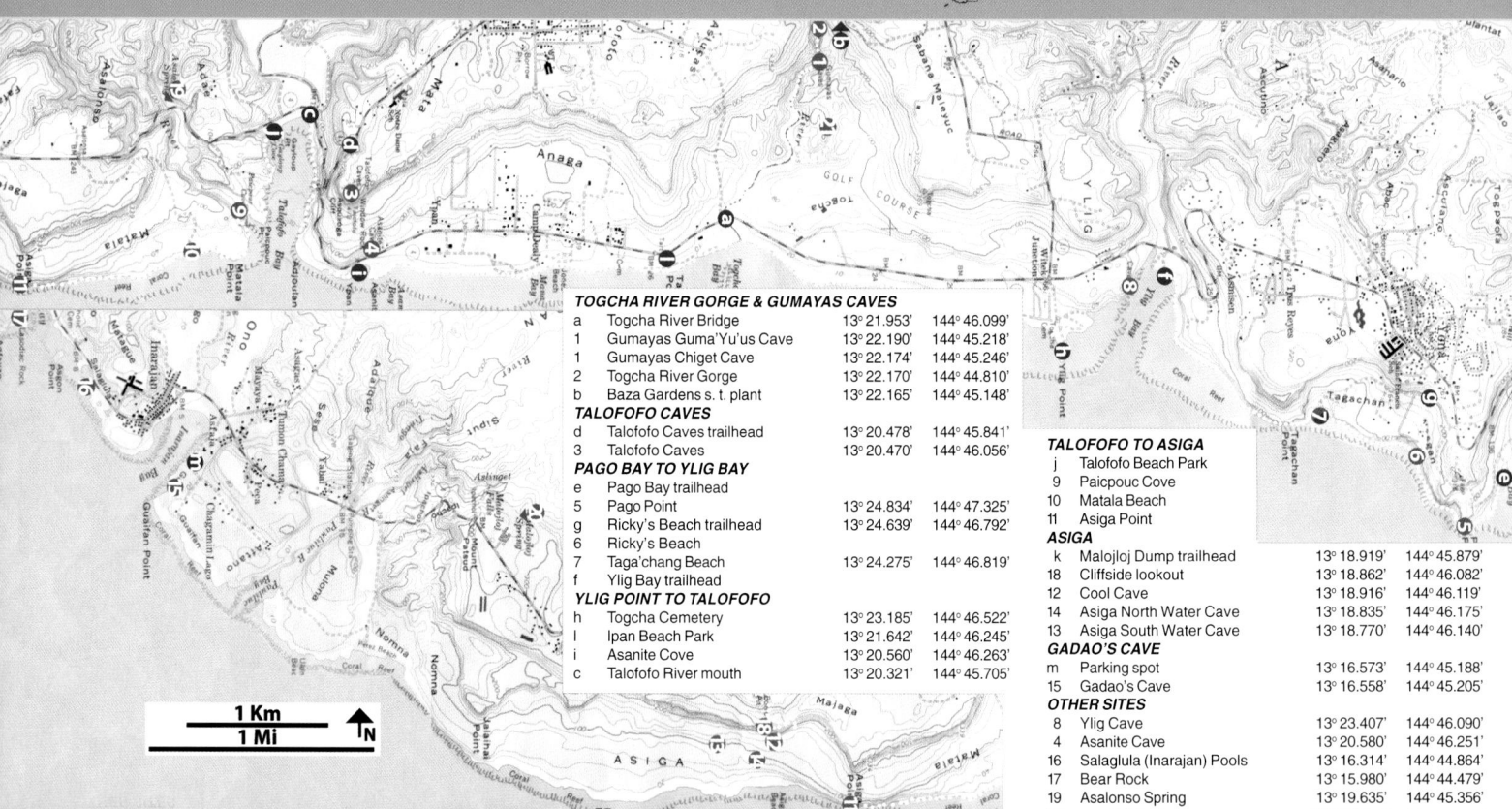

TOGCHA RIVER GORGE & GUMAYAS CAVES

a	Togcha River Bridge	13° 21.953'	144° 46.099'
1	Gumayas Guma'Yu'us Cave	13° 22.190'	144° 45.218'
1	Gumayas Chiget Cave	13° 22.174'	144° 45.246'
2	Togcha River Gorge	13° 22.170'	144° 44.810'
b	Baza Gardens s. t. plant	13° 22.165'	144° 45.148'

TALOFOFO CAVES

d	Talofofo Caves trailhead	13° 20.478'	144° 45.841'
3	Talofofo Caves	13° 20.470'	144° 46.056'

PAGO BAY TO YLIG BAY

e	Pago Bay trailhead		
5	Pago Point	13° 24.834'	144° 47.325'
g	Ricky's Beach trailhead	13° 24.639'	144° 46.792'
6	Ricky's Beach		
7	Taga'chang Beach	13° 24.275'	144° 46.819'
f	Ylig Bay trailhead		

YLIG POINT TO TALOFOFO

h	Togcha Cemetery	13° 23.185'	144° 46.522'
l	Ipan Beach Park	13° 21.642'	144° 46.245'
i	Asanite Cove	13° 20.560'	144° 46.263'
c	Talofofo River mouth	13° 20.321'	144° 45.705'

TALOFOFO TO ASIGA

j	Talofofo Beach Park		
9	Paicpouc Cove		
10	Matala Beach		
11	Asiga Point		

ASIGA

k	Malojloj Dump trailhead	13° 18.919'	144° 45.879'
18	Cliffside lookout	13° 18.862'	144° 46.082'
12	Cool Cave	13° 18.916'	144° 46.119'
14	Asiga North Water Cave	13° 18.835'	144° 46.175'
13	Asiga South Water Cave	13° 18.770'	144° 46.140'

GADAO'S CAVE

m	Parking spot	13° 16.573'	144° 45.188'
15	Gadao's Cave	13° 16.558'	144° 45.205'

OTHER SITES

8	Ylig Cave	13° 23.407'	144° 46.090'
4	Asanite Cave	13° 20.580'	144° 46.251'
16	Salaglula (Inarajan) Pools	13° 16.314'	144° 44.864'
17	Bear Rock	13° 15.980'	144° 44.479'
19	Asalonso Spring	13° 19.635'	144° 45.356'

1 Km
1 Mi
N

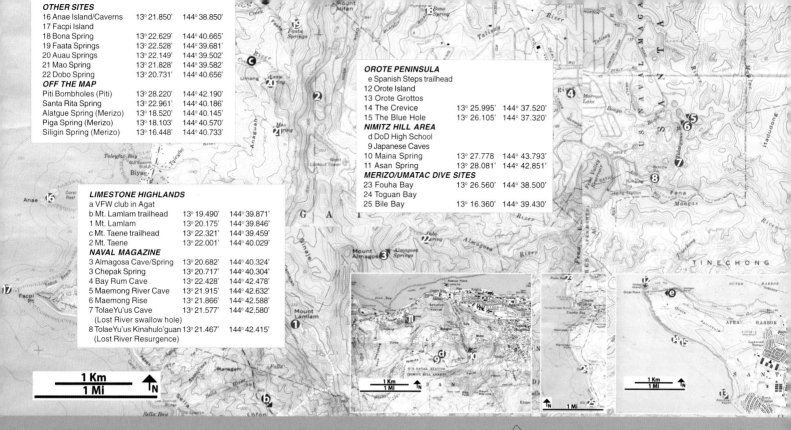

OTHER SITES

16 Anae Island/Caverns	13° 21.850'	144° 38.850'
17 Facpi Island		
18 Bona Spring	13° 22.629'	144° 40.665'
19 Faata Springs	13° 22.528'	144° 39.681'
20 Auau Springs	13° 22.149'	144° 39.502'
21 Mao Spring	13° 21.828'	144° 39.582'
22 Dobo Spring	13° 20.731'	144° 40.656'

OFF THE MAP

Piti Bombholes (Piti)	13° 28.220'	144° 42.190'
Santa Rita Spring	13° 22.961'	144° 40.186'
Alatgue Spring (Merizo)	13° 18.520'	144° 40.145'
Piga Spring (Merizo)	13° 18.103'	144° 40.570'
Siligin Spring (Merizo)	13° 16.448'	144° 40.733'

OROTE PENINSULA

e Spanish Steps trailhead		
12 Orote Island		
13 Orote Grottos		
14 The Crevice	13° 25.995'	144° 37.520'
15 The Blue Hole	13° 26.105'	144° 37.320'

NIMITZ HILL AREA

d DoD High School		
9 Japanese Caves		
10 Maina Spring	13° 27.778'	144° 43.793'
11 Asan Spring	13° 28.081'	144° 42.851'

MERIZO/UMATAC DIVE SITES

23 Fouha Bay	13° 26.560'	144° 38.500'
24 Toguan Bay		
25 Bile Bay	13° 16.360'	144° 39.430'

LIMESTONE HIGHLANDS

a VFW club in Agat		
b Mt. Lamlam trailhead	13° 19.490'	144° 39.871'
1 Mt. Lamlam	13° 20.175'	144° 39.846'
c Mt. Taene trailhead	13° 22.321'	144° 39.459'
2 Mt. Taene	13° 22.001'	144° 40.029'

NAVAL MAGAZINE

3 Almagosa Cave/Spring	13° 20.682'	144° 40.324'
3 Chepak Spring	13° 20.717'	144° 40.304'
4 Bay Rum Cave	13° 22.428'	144° 42.478'
5 Maemong River Cave	13° 21.915'	144° 42.632'
6 Maemong Rise	13° 21.866'	144° 42.588'
7 TolaeYu'us Cave	13° 21.577'	144° 42.580'
(Lost River swallow hole)		
8 TolaeYu'us Kinahulo'guan	13° 21.467'	144° 42.415'
(Lost River Resurgence)		

1 Km
1 Mi
N

Glossary

Active stream passage: Cave passage with a permanent or ephemeral stream flow.

Aggressive water: Water capable of dissolving limestone.

Allogenic: Water flowing from non-karst areas (e.g. streams or rivers on volcanic terrain).

Alluviated: Covered by alluvium (mud, sand, and other stream deposits).

Aquifer: A body of rock capable of storing and transmitting underground water.

Aragonite: A $CaCO_3$ mineral, less common than calcite.

Autogenic: Water falling as rain directly on karst rocks.

Barrier coral reef: Coral reef growing away from and parallel to the shore.

Beachrock: Consolidated and lithified beach sand, transformed into rock.

Bedrock: In caves, original rock body in which the cave was dissolved.

Benthic: Bottom zone in oceans, lakes; also, a bottom-dwelling organism.

Bioerosion: Erosion of rock by living organisms, usually marine.

Bioerosional groove: A horizontal notch in coastal rocks, made by bioerosion.

Biokarst: Karst features created by living organisms.

Blind valleys: Stream valleys, abruptly closed at their lower end (e.g. by cliffs); may be dry or contain sinking streams.

Blue-green algae: Type of primitive photosynthetic bacteria.

Calcareous algae: Algae that deposit $CaCO_3$ in their tissue.

Calcareous sand: Sand made of shells and parts of organisms (made of $CaCO_3$) and eroded limestone.

Calcite: The most common $CaCO_3$ mineral; the main constituent of limestone.

Cave: A natural underground cavity large enough to be entered by a person.

Cave pearl: A smooth rounded speleothem found in shallow hollows into which water drips.

Cavern: Cave or a very large cave room.

Cenote: A sinkhole reaching groundwater level and containing a permanent freshwater pool.

Chamber: The largest cavities in caves, having considerable width and length.

Cliff retreat: Landward erosion of a cliff by ocean waves (a cliff gets undercut and collapses).

Cockpit karst: Area densely covered by sinkholes, separated by narrow limestone ridges.

Collapse sinkhole: A sinkhole formed by the collapse of an underground void.

Column: A speleothem made by the joining of a stalactite and a stalagmite, creating a single floor-to-ceiling formation.

Conduit: An underground stream course.

Conduit flow: Rapid flow of groundwater via cave passages and other conduits.

Cone of depression: Lowering of the water table around a production well.

Glossary

Detrital limestone: Limestone made from $CaCO_3$ detritus (plankton shells, corals, mollusk shell fragments, etc.)

Diffuse flow: Slow flow of groundwater via pores and other small holes in rock.

Discharge: Outflow of water from an aquifer.

Dissolution: see solution.

Drawdown sinkhole: A sinkhole formed by slow subsidence in an area where water stored in the epikarst preferentially moves into the aquifer.

Encrusting algae: Algae that form a hard surface on a substrate.

Ephemeral stream: A temporary stream, flowing only during and following rain events.

Epikarst: Upper, heavily weathered layer (often soil covered) in a karst terrain.

Evapotranspiration: Sum of water evaporation from land surface and transpiration from plants.

Fault: Fracture in rock along which separated rock bodies have moved.

Flank margin cave: Coastal caves created by dissolution by an aggressive mixture of fresh and salty groundwater.

Flashy spring: A spring with a discharge which is not constant, but varies with time and increases following rains.

Flowstone: A cave deposit usually made of calcite, formed by trickles of water.

Flowstone partition: Extensive deposits of flowstone, which can create walls separating cave rooms.

Foraminifera: A common type of planktonic or benthic single-celled organism, which builds shells out of calcium carbonate.

Fossils: Animal or plant remains or traces in rocks or sediments.

Fracture: A crack in a rock.

Fringing coral reef: Coral reef, growing adjacent to the shoreline.

Groundwater: Underground water.

Groundwater table: see water table.

Halocline: An area of sudden change in water salinity (e.g. a boundary between salt water and fresh water).

Helictite: Irregular, gravity-defying, curved or angular speleothem.

High-level spring: A spring flowing above sea level.

Inflow cave: A cave with a stream flowing into it.

Karren: Minor, small-scale etchings on the surface of karst rocks, often covered by soil.

Karrenfeld: Area of exposed limestone bedrock, dominated by karren, and not covered by soil (German "karren field").

Karst: A terrain where surface drainage has been partially or entirely diverted underground via characteristic landforms such as sinkholes and caves (from Serbo-Croat and Slovene words "krš" and "kras," referring to bare, rocky terrain).

99

Glossary

Lithification: The process of sediments turning into rock.

Mixing zone: Area where two different waters mix (e.g. at the bottom of a freshwater lens where freshwater and underlying seawater mix).

Mushroom rock: A boulder or an island with a bioerosional groove around its circumference at sea level, giving it a mushroom shape.

Outflow cave: A cave from which a stream emerges, but cannot be followed upstream to the surface.

Passage: A cavity much longer than it is wide or high.

Perched water: A body of surface water or groundwater above sea level (e.g. a pond in a clogged sinkhole).

Phreatic dissolution surfaces: Cave wall and ceiling surfaces smoothened by dissolution in a flooded environment.

Phreatic tube/passage: A cave passage with smooth surfaces, elliptical or circular in cross-section, formed under flooded conditions.

Phreatic water: Water below the groundwater table; in the phreatic zone.

Phreatic zone: The zone below the groundwater table, in which all voids in rock are completely saturated by groundwater.

Pinnacle karst: A tropical landscape of nearly vertical-sided spires.

Planktonic: Free-floating.

Porosity: Property of rock having small voids.

Precipitation: A change from gaseous state to liquid, or from liquid (dissolved) state to solid state.

Progradational collapse: The process of enlarging a cave or void upward by consecutive collapses.

Pseudokarst: Landforms resembling karst, but not made by karst processes.

Recharge: The process of adding water to an aquifer; also the quantity of water added to an aquifer.

Reef limestone: Limestone originally deposited as a reef.

Resurgence: A spring where a stream, which has a course higher up on the surface, reappears lower down.

Rimstone: Deposits formed by precipitation from water flowing over the edge of a pool.

Saltwater intrusion: The contamination of a freshwater lens by salty groundwater.

Saturated water: Water that has dissolved as much limestone as possible under given conditions.

Sea cave: A cave formed in coastal cliffs, by the action of waves.

Sea level stillstands: Times of stable sea levels in the past.

Sediment: Material deposited by wind, water or ice, or precipitated from water.

Sedimentary rocks: Rocks formed by lithification of sediment or precipitated from water, inorganically or by organisms.

Shelter cave: A small cave fully penetrated by daylight.

Glossary

Siphon: A water-filled passage with a "U" profile.

Soda straw: A thin, tubular stalactite.

Soil pipes: Soil-filled pits in the epikarst.

Solution: The process in which a solid changes to liquid, by combining with water.

Solution basin (or solution pan): A basin dissolved in limestone by the pooling of water.

Speleothem: A cave deposit, most commonly formed of calcite.

Spring: The natural flow of water from rock.

Stalactite: A conical or cylindrical speleothem hanging from a cave ceiling or wall.

Stalagmite: A speleothem projecting upward from a cave floor.

Stream cave: A cave formed by an underground stream.

Subaerial: Exposed to air.

Swallow hole: A shaft or a depression in which a surface stream disappears underground.

Traversable passage: A passage large enough for a person to enter.

Unsaturated water: Water that can dissolve limestone, because it contains less dissolved $CaCO_3$ than it can carry under given conditions.

Vadose bypasses: Voids in the vadose zone that allow rapid flow of water.

Vadose canyon: A deep elongate cavity, cut by running water.

Vadose flow: Water flowing through caves as free-surface streams.

Vadose seepage: Water moving mainly downward through pores and cracks in the vadose zone.

Vadose shafts: Long, vertical voids in the vadose zone.

Vadose water: Water in the vadose zone.

Vadose zone: The zone above the groundwater table where rock voids are partly filled with air, through which water descends by gravity.

Void: A hole in a rock.

Water table: The surface between phreatic water, which completely fills the voids in rock, and ground air; the top boundary of a groundwater body.

UNIT ABBREVIATIONS

m - meter
km - kilometer
m^2 - square meter
km^2 - square kilometer
cm^3 - cubic centimeter, cc
g - gram
L - liter
ft. - foot
mi. - mile
°C - degrees Celsius
°F - degrees Fahrenheit

UNIT CONVERSIONS

1m = 3.28 ft.
1km = 0.62 mi.
$1m^2$ = 10.76 sq. ft.
$1km^2$ = 0.38 sq. mi.
1L = 0.26 gal.

Index to Places

Recommended Readings

KARST GEOLOGY & HYDROLOGY

Ford, D.C., and P.W. Williams. 1989. *Karst Geomorphology and Hydrology*. Winchester, MA: Unwin Hyman.

Klimchouk, A.B., D.C. Ford, A.N. Palmer, and W. Dreybrodt, eds. 2000. *Speleogenesis: Evolution of Karst Aquifers*. Huntsville, AL: Nat. Spel. Soc.

White, W.B. 1988. *Geomorphology and Hydrology of Karst Terrains*. New York: Oxford Press.

ISLAND KARST

Martin, J.B., C.M. Wicks, and I.D. Sasowsky, eds. 2002. *Hydrogeology and Biology of Post-Paleozoic Carbonate Aquifers*. Charles Town, WV: Karst Waters Inst.

Mylroie, J.E., and J.L. Carew. 1995. Karst Development on Carbonate Islands. In *Unconformities and Porosity in Carbonate Strata*. Tulsa, OK: American Association of Petroleum Geologists.

Vacher, H.L., and T.M. Quinn, eds. 1997. *Geology and Hydrogeology of Carbonate Islands*, Vol. 54 of *Developments in Sedimentology*. Amsterdam: Elsevier.

GEOLOGY OF GUAM

Emery, K.O. 1962. *Marine Geology of Guam*. U.S.G.S. Prof. Paper 403-B. Washington, D.C.: U.S.G.S.

Siegrist, H.G., and R.H. Randall. 1992. Carbonate Geology of Guam. 7th Int. Coral Reef Symp., Vol. 2:1195-1216.

Tracey, J.I., Jr., S.O. Schlanger, J.T. Stark, D.B. Doan, and H.G. May. 1964. *General Geology of Guam*. U.S.G.S. Prof. Paper 403-A. Washington, D.C.: U.S.G.S.

Ward, P.E., S.H. Hoffard, and D.A. Davis. 1965. *Hydrology of Guam*. U.S.G.S. Prof. Paper 403-H. Wash., D.C.: U.S.G.S.

KARST OF GUAM

Mylroie, J.E., J.W. Jenson, J.M.U. Jocson, and M. Lander. 1999. *Karst Geology and Hydrology of Guam*. Mangilao, Guam: WERI, University of Guam.

Mylroie, J. E., J.W. Jenson, D. Taboroši, J.M.U. Jocson, D.T. Vann, and C. Wexel. 2001. Karst Features of Guam in Terms of a General Model of Carbonate Island Karst. Journal of Cave and Karst Studies 63:9-22.

CAVING

Rea, T. 1987. Caving Basics. Huntsville, AL: Nat. Spel. Soc.

McClurg, D.R. 1986. Adventures of Caving. Huntsville, AL: Nat. Spel. Soc.

Howes, C. 1997. Images Below: A Manual of Underground and Flash Photography. Huntsville, AL: Nat. Spel. Soc.

Smith, B., and A. Padgett. 1996. On Rope. Huntsville, AL: Nat. Spel. Soc.

Dasher, G. R. 1994. On Station. Huntsville, AL: Nat. Spel. Soc.

OTHER

Lotz, D. 2000. *The Best Tracks on Guam*, 2nd edition. Barrigada, Guam: Making Tracks.

Randall, R.H., and J. Holloman. 1974. *Coastal Survey of Guam*. Mangilao, Guam: Marine Lab, University of Guam.

Rock, T. 1999. *Diving & Snorkeling, Guam & Yap*. Victoria, Australia: Lonely Planet Publications.

105

Hydrologic Map of Guam

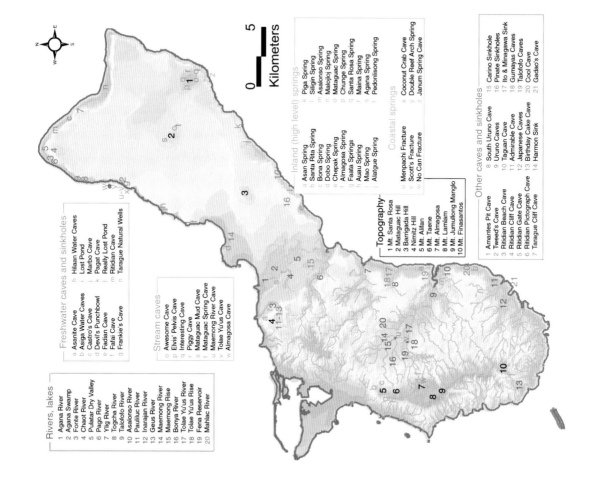

Kilometers

0   5

Rivers, lakes

1 Agana River
2 Agana Swamp
3 Fonte River
4 Chaot River
5 Pulatar Dry Valley
6 Pago River
7 Ylig River
8 Togcha River
9 Talofofo River
10 Asalonso River
11 Pauliluc River
12 Inarajan River
13 Geus River
14 Maemong River
15 Maemong Rise
16 Bonya River
17 Tolae Yu'us River
18 Tolae Yu'us Rise
19 Fena Reservoir
20 Mahlac River

Freshwater caves and sinkholes

a Asanite Cave
b Asiga Water Caves
c Castro's Cave
d Devil's Punchbowl
e Fadian Cave
f Fafai Cave
g Frankie's Cave
h Hilaan Water Caves
i Lost Pond
j Marbo Cave
k Pagat Cave
l Really Lost Pond
m Ritidian Cave
n Tarague Natural Wells

Stream caves

o Awesome Cave
p Elvis' Pelvis Cave
q Interesting Cave
r Piggy Cave
s Mataguac Mud Cave
t Mataguac Spring Cave
u Maemong River Cave
v Tolae Yu'us Cave
w Almagosa Cave

Topography

1 Mt. Santa Rosa
2 Mataguac Hill
3 Barrigada Hill
4 Nimitz Hill
5 Mt. Alifan
6 Mt. Taene
7 Mt. Almagosa
8 Mt. Lamlam
9 Mt. Jumullong Manglo
10 Mt. Finasantos

Inland (high level) springs

a Asan Spring
b Santa Rita Spring
c Bona Spring
d Dobo Spring
e Chepak Spring
f Almagosa Spring
g Faata Springs
h Auau Spring
i Mao Spring
j Alatgue Spring
k Piga Spring
l Siligin Spring
m Asalonso Spring
n Malojloj Spring
o Mataguac Spring
p Chunge Spring
q Santa Rosa Spring
r Maina Spring
s Agana Spring
t Pedonlisong Spring

Coastal springs

u Menpachi Fracture
v Scott's Fracture
w No Can Fracture
x Coconut Crab Cave
y Double Reef Arch Spring
z Janum Spring Cave

Other caves and sinkholes

1 Amantes Pit Cave
2 Tweed's Cave
3 Ritidian Beach Cave
4 Ritidian Cliff Cave
5 Ritidian Gate Cave
6 Ritidian Pictograph Cave
7 Tarague Cliff Cave
8 South Uruno Cave
9 Uruno Caves
10 Taguan Cave
11 Admirable Cave
12 Japanese Caves
13 Birthday Cake Cave
14 Harmon Sink
15 Carino Sinkhole
16 Pinate Sinkholes
17 Ito & Minagawa Sink
18 Gumayas Caves
19 Talofofo Caves
20 Cool Cave
21 Gadao's Cave

Coastal Features of Guam

Bays, coves, beaches

1 Agana Bay
2 Ypao Beach
3 Tumon Bay/Beach
4 Gun Beach
5 Fafai Beach
6 Guma Fahou
7 Ague Cove
8 Haputo Beach
9 Frankie's Cove
10 Double Reef Beach
11 Falcona Beach
12 Uruno Beach
13 Ritidian Beach
14 Jinapsan Beach

15 Star Sand Beach
16 Tarague Beach
17 Sasaiyan Embayment
18 Fadian Cove
19 Pago Bay
20 Ricky's Beach
21 Taga'chang Beach
22 Ylig Bay
23 Ipan Beach
24 Asanite Cove
25 Talofofo Bay
26 Paicpouc Cove
27 Matala Beach
28 Nomna Bay

29 Pauliluc Bay
30 Inarajan Bay
31 Aglrayan Bay
32 Atao Beach
33 Bile Bay
34 Tougan Bay
35 Fouha Bay
36 Cetti Bay
37 Sella Bay
38 Dadi Beach
39 Tipalo Beach
40 Gab Gab
41 Glass Breakwater
42 Family Beach

Reefs, sea caves, submarine sites

1 Matt's Cave
2 Shark's Hole
3 Matt's Freshwater Cave
4 Double Reef
5 Pagat Natural Arch
6 Salagjula Pools
7 Cocos Lagoon/ Reef

8 Anae Caverns
9 Orote Caverns
10 Blue Hole
11 Crevice
12 Orote Channel
13 Luminao Reef
14 Piti Bombholes

Coastal cliffline points

1 Amantes Point
2 Tanguisson Point
3 Hilaan Point
4 Pugua Point
5 Uruno Point
6 Achae Point
7 Ritidian Point
8 Pajon Point
9 Jinapsan Point
10 Mergagan Point
11 Tagua Point
12 Pati Point
13 Latte Point
14 Lafac Point
15 Anao Point
16 Mati Point

17 Catalina Point
18 Janum Point
19 Lujuna Point
20 Pagat Point
21 Campanaya Point
22 Taguan Point
23 Fadian Point
24 Taogam Point
25 Pago Point
26 Ylig Point
27 Tartuguan Point
28 Matala Point
29 Asiga Point
30 Bear Rock
31 Facpi Point
32 Orote Point

Guam's fringing islets

1 Jeff's Islet
2 Aspon Point Islet
3 Gujien Islet West
4 Gujien Islet East
5 Agrigan Island
6 Fofos Island
7 Asgadao Island
8 Babe Island
9 Cocos Island
10 Facpi Island
11 Anae Island

12 Bangi Island
13 Yona Island
14 Alutom Island
15 Pelagi Islet South
16 Pelagi Islet North
17 Neye Island
18 Orote Island
19 Orote Channel Islets
20 Noddy Islet
21 Camel Rock
22 Alupat Island

0 ___ 5

Kilometers

Road Map of Guam